Rhythms
of Change

Mary Saunders

Rhythms of Change
Reclaiming Your Health Using Ancient Wisdom and
Your Own Common Sense
Mary Saunders

Publisher:
Hidden Needle Press
PO Box 1435
Makawao, HI 96768

First Edition September, 2014
Second Printing March, 2015
Third Printing November, 2016
ISBN: 978-0-615-93145-6
Library of Congress Control Number: 2014946689

www.MarySaundersHealth.com

Printed in the USA

For Whitfield,

For Martin

ACKNOWLEDGMENTS

I owe an enormous debt of gratitude to my editor, Evelyn Leigh. She brought out the best in this material with her insightful questions and thoughtful editing.

Thank you, Patricia Appelfeller at *www.appelfellerarts.com* for your artist's eye and the elegant graphic design, formatting, and cover you created for this book.

A heartfelt thanks to Julie Predki-Weber, LAc., for her editing, research assistance, and consistently helpful feedback.

Thank you Whitfield Reaves, Martin Reaves, Helen Saunders, Sandy Cottriel, Livia Hall, Ariana Ross, Meghan Rogers, Cheng Hsi Ho, Charlotte Hansen, Jeni Driver, Lorena Monda, and Marlene Merritt for your contributions to the book.

To my many teachers, patients, and friends who have trusted me over the years. Knowing each one of you has enriched my life, and I am deeply grateful.

TABLE OF CONTENTS

PART ONE

THE ANCIENT WISDOM OF THE FIVE PHASES OF CHANGE

PART TWO

COMMON SENSE SUGGESTIONS AND PROTOCOLS FOR THE FIVE PHASES

PART THREE

RESOURCES

Rhythms
of Change

Reclaiming Your Health
Using Ancient Wisdom and
Your Own Common Sense

Mary Saunders

Hidden Needle Press
Boulder, Colorado

INTRODUCTION

Come, come, whoever you are! Wanderer, worshipper, lover of leaving. Ours is not a caravan of despair. It doesn't matter if you've broken your vow a thousand times, still and yet again come!

— Rumi

I have been in practice as a licensed acupuncturist for almost 30 years and have seen thousands of patients. This book began as a response to my patients' questions and desire to understand more about their experiences with Oriental medicine in my clinic. I have since embraced the idea of sharing what I have learned in a book as a way to open a door that could possibly lead you, the reader, to reconnect with your own inner knowing, and thus your health, in the broadest sense of the word.

To effectively treat my patients, I have found practical ways to adapt the ancient wisdom of Oriental medicine to address the way we currently live. It is the way of this traditional medicine—and one of the reasons it is so effective—to observe and treat an individual as one integrated, interconnected system, not a list of unrelated symptoms. At the same time, Oriental medicine views everything as part of a pattern of relationship. From the early days of my practice, I have focused on treating my patients as individuals. But it took me many years to see the patterns emerging in the clinic population as a whole that reflect on the way we are now living, often to the detriment of our health and well being.

Over the last several decades, humans have somehow managed to do the unthinkable: We have distanced ourselves so effectively from nature, the body, and our inner knowing that we can no longer remember how to access the wisdom within us. This inherent wisdom is what I mean by common sense. We all have the ability to naturally take in information and understand how it fits into our life. When we are observing and reflecting on cause and effect, we can be in dynamic relationship with all aspects of ourselves and with the world around us.

However, many of us try to pretend that the rhythms of nature do not apply to us, that somehow we are not bound by the universal laws that have governed human beings forever. We have lost the awareness of our connection to nature and thus to ourselves. We no longer know the experience of being whole, of our bodies being one with our hearts and minds. We do not trust the body and the wisdom it tries to convey about how to live more deeply. We do not trust our own experience. This loss of connection to something sacred and essential to our nature as human beings creates myriad forms of disease, physical as well as emotional, and has brought us to a way of living that in many cases no longer makes any sense.

In recent years, the way patients present in the acupuncture clinic has been changing quite remarkably. The symptoms and imbalances I see are more chronic and complex than they were when I began my practice in 1986. So much of the suffering I encounter now comes not from a lack of information, but rather from us ignoring the simple yet profound wisdom of nature and our own common sense. I believe that every symptom is a sign post that we can choose to follow or ignore. We can access this wisdom within ourselves, yet we avoid, neglect, and ignore it to the point of rendering ourselves deaf to its urgent calls. Perhaps this is why many of the dietary and lifestyle practices I consider "common sense" are not self-evident to patients who have largely lost touch with their own inner knowing.

Oriental medicine encompasses the use of acupuncture, herbal medicine, dietary therapy, lifestyle modifications, meditation, and exercises such as tai chi and qi gong to help us balance, and reconnect to, our bodies. The techniques used vary from one practitioner to another, but the underlying principles are based on centuries of observation, practice, and a profound understanding of the unity of body, mind, and spirit. I use many of the above techniques in my practice, along with the other essential resources I have been given— my intuition and common sense.

Oriental medical theory uses metaphors to describe five qualities of energy or elemental factors that are in constant relationship with one another in nature and within us. These are what I call the five phases of change: Earth, Wood, Fire, Metal, and Water. Each of us has all five phases within us, to a greater or lesser degree, all the time. They are all happening simultaneously. The characteristics of one phase or another may be more pronounced at a given time depending on age, environment, or life circumstances. Most of us were born with a tendency toward a particular constitution, one that might manifest more Earth than Fire traits, for example. However, it is important to not identify too closely with one particular phase, as it will keep you from seeing the influences—and meeting the challenges—of the other phases.

In this book, in order to make the wisdom of the five phases of change more accessible, I have included patient stories and examples from my own life to illustrate the ideas I present. I have experienced the process of change I describe; my knowledge is more than conceptual. I have lived the extremes of the imbalances of each of the five phases of change, and my assimilation of the teachings has not always been graceful. I intentionally show you my foibles and my many blind spots to illustrate that we all make mistakes and we can use them to evolve. My hope is that this book will be a small light showing you one way back to yourself, back to your own common sense and natural intuition.

The process of change is not linear, but rather rhythmic and gradual. We do not automatically go from one phase to the next in the cycle. Think of the rhythmic ebb and flow of the tides. The gravitational pulls among the earth, the moon, and the sun dictate the tides. The body and psyche are subject to similar influences from natural phenomena, the power of the unconscious, and the pull of the soul reaching for its highest evolution. We may not be consciously aware of these influences, but they are there, and we can rely on them to move and change us, just as happens with the ebb and flow of the tides. Sometimes we move in what seems a haphazard fashion, leaping over one or more phases at a time, only to return to learn their lessons further down the path. For some the process is more of a spiral, of meeting the challenges of each phase in turn, and then going through the rhythms of change yet again but at a higher level of personal growth. It is usually only in retrospect that we can see how all has been woven together in this unique pattern that is our life.

This cyclical, rhythmic repetition is what allows for authentic transformation and sustained change. The intuitive knowing within each of us, men and women alike, teaches us to be receptive and yielding to life, to stay connected to and trust nature and our bodies, and to allow times of rest, darkness, and not-knowing, as well as active, light-filled, focused times.

We move with the rhythms of change, spiraling ever closer to a truer version of ourselves: The body gains more energy, the mind becomes clearer. We make better decisions, connect with our purpose and our place in the community, and feel inspired to serve something other than our own interests.

My experience has taught me that life is better able to support us when we consciously participate in our own unfolding. When you know what phase you are in, you will have the necessary information to understand what the challenges are and the most effective strategy to meet them. For example, the Wood phase is expansive, a time to make creative plans and clear decisions to move forward in life. The energy of the Metal phase is contractive; this is a time to reflect inwardly on your values and make the often difficult choices to let go of what is nonessential to your growth. Knowing that the door to outer expansion is closed in the Metal phase, you do not waste precious time and energy banging your head against it. Rather, you use the energy available to deepen and further other aspects of yourself.

All the phases are equally valuable and need to be lived through to become more wholly yourself. *Rhythms of Change* is a tool I offer to help you know where you are and thus be more successful at moving through all the phases of life. I am absolutely certain that if you put your inner knowing into practice in your daily life, you can take these proven, practical steps toward more balance and satisfaction in your life.

To Change or Not to Change?

Talking, talking, always talking, will get you nowhere. It is your actions, repeated over and over, that will determine the quality of your life and death.

—Yoga Sutras

For 30 years, I have watched my patients, my friends, and myself struggle to change our habits around relationships, diet, exercise, and stress in order to improve our health. If we want to change our lives so badly, why can we not just do it? Why are we unable to let go of behaviors that keep us from getting what we need? We all know it is not simply a question of willpower, of forcing ourselves to do something we know will be good for us. We have most likely tried this approach numerous times, and it just does not work over the long term.

For change to be possible, we must begin by facing our circumstances as honestly as we can and then accepting them. I am not suggesting you resign yourself to your current situation, but do accept the truth of it as it is now, in this moment. Please do not start to gear up and mobilize to change yourself. That hasn't worked before so do it differently this time. Relax into yourself, accept yourself just as you are now, allow yourself to simply be. Be open, receptive, and curious as you continue this journey.

Remember, change does not necessarily happen in a linear or dramatic way. I have learned to be wary of the patient or friend who tells me that a brief encounter, a new supplement, or a weekend workshop has changed her life. I have experienced it myself too many times: We are desperate to change, to be different, and to find relief from our suffering, so we hope this new person or technique will be the thing that finally saves us from ourselves. Of course, miracles do happen, but most of us have to do the work over time to make change happen. The "ah ha!" moments we experience are essential to the process of change, but we must then digest the new information. We revert to old patterns and then come back to the visceral experience of transformation in the body. For some this may happen in weeks or months, but for most of us, it is a gradual, spiraling process that may take years to fully integrate.

> *We cannot change anything until we accept it.*
> *Condemnation does not liberate, it oppresses.*
>
> —Carl Jung

In his book, *Change or Die: The Three Keys to Change at Work and in Life,* Alan Deutschman states that the scientifically studied odds are nine-to-one against us changing the behaviors we know make us sick. Excess stress, smoking, drinking, improper eating, and lack of exercise are the five main behaviors we know create disease. We have heard it many times: Change these behaviors or die. What do most of us do? We choose to either live sick or die. This is so counterintuitive, yet obviously true, that it should make us curious about what is going on.

I realized there was a profound truth mirrored in Deutschman's writing. I looked deeply at my own life and my experience with thousands of patients, and saw that his three keys to change apply to most of us. What I have come to understand is that in order for us to make changes that last, we have to change who we are. It is not enough to do things differently; we need to be different.

Deutschman calls the three keys to change "the three Rs":

RELATE. "Form a new, emotional relationship with a person or community that inspires and sustains hope."

REPEAT. "This new relationship helps you learn, practice, and master the new habits and skills that you'll need. It takes a lot of repetition over time before new patterns of behavior become automatic and seem natural, until you act the new way without even thinking about it."

REFRAME. "The new relationship helps you learn new ways of thinking about your situation and your life. Ultimately, you look at the world in a way that would have been so foreign to you that it wouldn't have made any sense before you changed."

I have adapted the three Rs for my own use, based on the understanding of the rhythmic process of change that I have developed during my years of clinical and spiritual practice, and added a fourth, essential R to the formula.

RECEPTIVITY leads to Relationship. Being receptive to life is the ground of all healing, transformation, and change. Receptivity is essential, yet many of us are completely unaware of the myriad ways we resist being open to what life wants to give us. Allow yourself to receive the experiences, emotions, ideas, and relationships life sends you to guide the next step on your journey.

REMEMBRANCE leads to Repetition. Come back to yourself each time you forget to practice the behaviors that support your dreams, aspirations, purpose, and goals. Do not waste time beating yourself up for forgetting. Be gentle, knowing it is human to forget as well as to remember. If you are patient, and keep coming back to what you know you want, eventually it will be natural to repeat the behaviors that serve your highest self.

REFLECTION leads to Reframing. Many of us are in a hurry to change. We may believe we understand and thus quickly move on to the next thing. But if you have not reflected deeply on an idea or experience, you will not be able to grasp its specific relevance to you and to your current situation. You have to do the work that makes it yours, that makes it come alive within you. Allow whatever time is necessary to contemplate and reflect on your experiences until you truly understand their meaning to you. When you have grasped the specific meaning that is uniquely yours, reframing your worldview will be the natural outcome.

RETURN. Return to yourself, to the body, to nature, and to whatever helps you feel whole and at peace.

Notice how each concept builds on the one that came before:

1. Receive the relationships you need for your growth.

2. Remember that repeated contact and interaction in those relationships is what will integrate the new behaviors and make them part of who you are, not just what you do.

3. Reflect on what resonates and has meaning for you, and what does not, to eventually reframe your experience.

4. Return always to yourself, to the wisdom in your body and in your heart.

In this book, I will use these four Rs at the end of each of the five phases chapters to provide you with a strategy for implementing the suggestions for change outlined in that chapter. I encourage you to make the four Rs your own, using this model to come up with the most effective and creative strategies for yourself.

My Personal Journey of Change

> *The right way to wholeness is made up of fateful detours and wrong turnings.*
>
> **—Carl Jung**

I began my journey of change because my life demanded it of me. Not because I am especially disciplined, or strong willed, or possessed of any particular virtue I can claim for myself. Life gave me experiences, challenges, and dreams that pushed me to change, and I learned to be receptive, to listen and respond as best I could. It is my hope that my story helps you see how this process, the rhythms of change, works in very specific ways.

When this began, I was entirely unaware of the extent of the imbalances in my life. I gradually moved through the rhythms of change to a place of greater awareness and connection, in which I am now able to access my body's wisdom and my inner knowing to maintain an ever-changing relationship with each of the five phases. I cannot claim supreme balance, but I can say that more often than not I feel alive and connected to myself and to the world around me. And that is good enough for now!

I was raised in a family of five girls. My father loved us, and he also let us know he was deeply disappointed that he did not have a son. From the moment I was born, the fourth of five girls, I lived in an environment colored by my father's disappointment that I was female and he was surrounded by women.

At the age of 28, after months of mounting disquiet, I woke up from a dream in which a voice shouted to me: "Get out!" I left my marriage and Spain and moved to Austin, Texas, where I promptly became ill. The repressed emotions from my childhood, the prolonged stress of being disconnected from friends and family, living in a different culture, and speaking a foreign language, along with the excess consumption of wine, second-hand smoke, lack of exercise—and now a divorce—had finally caught up with me.

My body was saying "No" so loudly and clearly that I could ignore it no longer. I was being offered the opportunity to face the truth about myself and my life, to learn how my unconscious beliefs had led to choices and behaviors that had brought me to this moment, to this illness. A friend referred me to her acupuncturist, and I became aware of how the rhythms of change had started working within me.

Instead of resisting or ignoring this illness, I got curious and opened myself to change. It was the beginning of a time of grace in my life. People and opportunities presented themselves to me; I realized I merely had to say yes, to give myself permission, in order to receive assistance from others. It was a time of making connections and building new relationships, of being open to a new way of living. This receptivity, being open to life, is the principal requirement for transformation.

Friends from college offered housing, laughter, companionship, and an introduction to Jungian psychology, the *Tao Te Ching,* and the *I Ching,* or *Book of Changes.* For many months, I went every Friday afternoon for acupuncture treatment and became good friends with my practitioner. This time was not all ease and happiness, of course. I often felt sad or confused, not sure I could trust myself after the many unconscious decisions that had brought me to this point. I spent time alone, journaling and reflecting on my experiences and insights. I felt as though the wall separating me from my unconscious was quickly eroding, with many intense and powerful dreams showing me what lay beneath the surface.

I again had the support and encouragement of my generous friends when nine months later I moved to Santa Fe, New Mexico to attend a post graduate program in acupuncture and Oriental medicine. I had no money saved after my years in Spain, but the owner of the college believed in my potential and said I could pay him back later, which I did. Almost unimaginable, is it not, that he could be so generous and trusting of a stranger? Yet grace comes at the most unexpected moments, if we consent to it. We have a choice to be receptive and to say yes to grace when it is offered.

I studied the wisdom of Oriental medicine and Taoism. I learned dietary therapy, meridian pathways, and hundreds of acupuncture points. I learned to cook and eat whole foods and to observe the way my body responded to stress. I began to practice tai chi. I also struggled with loneliness, fatigue brought on by the high altitude, and self-doubt in the face of a family and entire culture that knew nothing about acupuncture, herbs, or Taoist philosophy. But over time I gained a sense of confidence that has enabled me to walk this rather solitary path.

When I finished the training in 1986, my practitioner friend invited me to work in his acupuncture clinic in Austin. He became my mentor and helped me greatly in my first years of practice. He referred patients to me and consulted with me on the tough cases. I still remember the fun we had as we talked over lunch at the original Whole Foods Market, where we also sent our patients who wanted to explore a healthier lifestyle.

I took the next step on my journey when I began an in-depth training in Hakomi therapy. The Hakomi tradition is rooted in the understanding that the body is the gateway to unconscious core beliefs that organize our experience on all levels, including our capacity for change and healing. For two years, a dear friend and I attended these weekend trainings in Houston. We laughed, cried, studied, and took care of each other as we lived through this intensely transformative experience.

When I was 34, I married Whitfield, and we had our son, Martin. This brought me to a period of much joy, change, and many challenges. We learned the discipline required by family life: Regular times for meals, naps, homework, bedtime; expansive joy and activity balanced with quiet time sitting around reading or doing nothing at all. It was the rhythmic, repetitive quality of our days—at times deeply nurturing and at others tedious—that taught us the multiple skills of being a family.

Again, I want to emphasize, it was not all rosy. Having a child brought up an even deeper layer in my psyche associated with my own mother. I experienced postpartum depression, as she had, and struggled with fatigue and my ability to take care of myself. I focused all my energy on caring for the baby, but did not have much left for myself or my husband. One night he came home after a long day at work to a "dinner" of cold carrots and rice. Remembering that makes us both laugh now, but at the time, it was a sign of how overwhelmed I was with the tremendous change in our lives.

What was wrong with me, I wondered, that simply being a mother and part of a family was so hard? With help from friends and a therapist, I saw that with each step I took toward becoming more whole, more was demanded of me. More relationships meant more responsibilities. I had naively thought that more growth equaled greater ease. This is a common misunderstanding. It is just not so, or at least not in my case. For me, growth has been more of a process of assuming greater and greater responsibility for self and others. Now I had to go deeper into my psyche and confront issues I had with nourishment, self-reliance, and my own sense of worthiness as a woman and a mother—not easy stuff, but essential to taking the next step.

It happened gradually over those next few years, but eventually my husband and son taught me to loosen up around my sense of duty and responsibility, to have more fun, enjoy exercise, and incorporate play and movement into my daily life. Now I can't imagine not exercising every day. Not because I should, but because I like to! Moving— walking, dancing, swimming, and doing yoga—makes me feel good.

Through these years I was an undisciplined, and yet devoted, spiritual seeker. As a young girl, I was drawn to the devotional quality I felt being with my mother in church. I sat alone in my tree house, daydreaming and singing to Jesus. Later, I practiced Buddhist meditation, did Jungian dream work, active imagination, and shamanic journeying. However, it was not until I was 44 years old that the next level of integration and change happened. I met my spiritual teacher and discovered the mystic tradition of Sufism. Here I found a clear reflection of my true nature in a tradition that honors the feminine and believes in direct experience of the divine. Now, daily meditation comes easily. It nourishes me on a profound level, so I am drawn to simply sit down and allow myself this pleasure, this time of silence and stillness.

Stepping onto that path brought unimaginable demands on my psyche and equally profound changes in my being. Yet again, this new step brought more growth and more responsibility. I focused attention on my acupuncture practice in Boulder, Colorado, co-founding one of the first community acupuncture clinics in the country and treating many more patients every week. I have written *Rhythms of Change* as an offering, as a way to give something back after all these years of receiving so much support for my own unfolding.

As I finish this book, I am turning 58. Going through this process has brought tremendous personal growth and fulfillment. All the relationships I have described, and so many more, repeated over time, have allowed me to heal my body and my wounded psyche and open to the tremendous love life has to offer. I have learned to easily incorporate sound nutrition, regular exercise, playfulness, meditation, and spaciousness for being into my daily life. When I reflect on all that has happened, I am a bit awed. I am a different person than I was at age 28, when my journey began. These experiences have allowed me to change, quite an exceptional feat—or an act of grace, as I understand it now.

All of this to say: I know it is hard to change, but I also know it is possible. It takes time—in my case, 30 years so far and still counting. At times you will experience the challenging aspects of the rhythms—anger, despair, and grief. There will be many detours and distractions, perhaps weeks or months in which it seems you are making no progress. Yet the mystery of the process will keep working. The challenges will be woven together with the kindness, joy, and inspiration you experience, helping you unfold if you will only allow and engage it. Life recreates itself continuously within you if you do not interfere. You simply must take the first step, and the universe will step in to assist.

How To Use This Book

Rhythms of Change is divided into three parts. In part one, I explain the ancient wisdom and underlying principles that guide Oriental medicine and the five phases of change. This information provides the essential foundation for creating a new way to be. Part two is the how-to portion of the book, presenting common sense lifestyle protocols and nutritional information to help you move toward balance in each of the phases. Part three offers additional information and resources.

Part One of this book takes you through each of the five phases of change, showing you the characteristics, issues, and inherent wisdom underlying each phase. The Earth phase looks at our relationship to nourishment, food, and the body's natural needs and limitations. Wood gets us in touch with our capacity to move forward in life creatively when we appropriately use the energy of self-assertion and anger. Fire asks us to tap into our passion and harness the energy of self-disciplined action to express our true selves in the world. Metal teaches us to know our values, allow inspiration to strengthen us, and both hold on and let go in life. The Water phase takes us to the power of the unconscious, to the depths of our being, where we cultivate self-knowledge and spiritual wisdom.

Each chapter in this part of the book addresses particular challenges (both emotional and physical) that I believe are central to moving toward balance in that phase. Each includes a list of balanced and imbalanced traits typical of that phase, and presents a case study illustrating some specific issues faced by a person with an imbalance in that phase.

Self-Assessment Questions. Each of the five chapters in part one includes a set of 10 questions designed to help you determine where you are on the continuum of balance and imbalance for that particular phase. These questions will help you focus your awareness on your own personal strengths and weaknesses within each phase.

For each set of questions, ask yourself: Which of the following essential qualities or behaviors do I embody now? If you can say yes more often than no (at least 80 percent of the time) to the questions, congratulations! You embody many of the essential qualities of balance in that phase. If not, please contemplate what needs to happen to get you to "yes" for that phase.

The ONE Thing. In addition to specific foods and balancing practices, each of the chapters in part one includes a recommendation for one essential thing to incorporate into your life to balance the energy of that phase. If you are willing to adopt this one simple behavior every day, you will create the literal foundation for your long-term health.

The ONE thing is really the energy of love disguised as simple behaviors: cooking and eating whole foods, giving yourself the strength and ease that come from movement, sleeping deeply to regenerate, mindfully breathing to bring yourself into union with the present moment, and giving yourself ample time to rest with unstructured downtime. These behaviors are all ways to show respect to the natural rhythms of change within you and to the greater wholeness of life itself.

I have chosen the ONE thing and the practices (see below) for each phase carefully, knowing the power for transformation they contain. They may seem simple in themselves, but they will create the foundation for profound change in your being if you move toward incorporating them into your daily life.

Addressing Resistance. Resistance is a natural part of growth. Needing to push against what is blocking our growth makes us stronger. This part of each chapter offers suggestions to help you learn to use your resistance to change by coming into relationship with it.

Practices. The practices suggested in these chapters are here to help you come into a deeper relationship with parts of yourself that you may be neglecting. This is a process that requires an attitude of open inquiry and nonviolence toward the self. Be gentle with any insight and awareness that wants to surface and with what you discover about yourself.

The Four Rs. Each chapter concludes with "four Rs" designed to help you allow the changes of that phase to move through your life.

Part Two offers practical suggestions on nutrition and protocols to move toward balance in each phase as well as address the imbalances common to each of the five phases. Here you will find specific protocols for physical issues typical of imbalance in each phase, as well as foods and behaviors that are helpful or best avoided. Also included in this part of the book is a discussion of stress and how to work with it to prevent negative effects in any phase of change.

Part Three includes the appendices, references, bibliography, and a note about the author.

As you read this book, please remember: Oriental medicine is not a rigid system; there is no definitive good or bad. There are simply actions and consequences to actions. Better physical and mental health means we are more flexible and relaxed and have more options available to us. It is not helpful to think, for example, "Sugar is bad" or "I shouldn't be angry." We do not want to become neurotic about food or our behavior, with ever more rules to follow. We want to invite in all aspects of ourselves and allow ourselves to be nourished in the truest sense.

Instead of a strict list of rules, appropriate action is more a matter of what works for your unique body at a particular moment in time. This is always changing, so we have to pay attention and change with the body! Whatever you do, it is not helpful to judge or be harsh with yourself. Rather, look to the wisdom of the ancients as well as your own common sense, and the changes will come.

Every moment is available for transformation. Join me now in coming back to the natural rhythms of change.

Note to the reader: Please listen to your own body and gather information to make the choices that are right for you and your family. Do not take this information as personal medical advice. It is always wise to consult with a qualified health practitioner before starting any new herbs, supplements, or dietary and lifestyle programs.

PART ONE

THE ANCIENT WISDOM
OF THE FIVE PHASES OF CHANGE

ANCIENT WISDOM OF ORIENTAL MEDICINE

Oriental medicine has developed over 2,000 years and is based on extensive observation of human beings and nature, critical thinking by highly respected physicians, and vast clinical experience. Ancient texts such as *Huangdi Neijing*, or *Inner Classic of the Yellow Emperor*, written in the second century BCE, gave clinicians material to work with, build on, and adapt. The medicine has continued to evolve up to modern times. Taoism, the patterns of relationship between yin and yang, and the five phases of change are the ancient wisdom underlying Oriental medicine.

The brilliance and effectiveness of Oriental medicine reside in the understanding that everything is interconnected, that no single part can be understood except in relation to the whole. Just as all parts of the body are connected through the circulatory, nervous, endocrine, and energetic meridian systems, each human being is connected to all other beings on the planet through the oceans, the air, and the earth we share. We are not separate. We are the oneness that exists in the universe. The shamans, healers, visionaries, and wise ones of ancient times and today know this and live accordingly, each in their own way.

To access this wisdom in ourselves, we can follow the Taoist practice of closely observing and looking for patterns and relationships, the connections among the various phases of change, and the balance between extremes. The practitioner of Oriental medicine learns to see relationships and patterns of disharmony and works to bring the whole person back into balance. You can use these insights to guide your journey to better health and a more conscious sense of your own wholeness.

TAOISM

Taoism is a philosophical tradition that emphasizes living in harmony with the Tao—natural law, or "the Way." Taoism is not a religion, but a way of living. One may be Christian, Buddhist, or a nonbeliever, and still benefit from the wisdom of the Tao. Taoism describes the way things naturally are, or the way things happen of themselves if left to their inherent nature, if we do not interfere. It is a very open ended system, allowing each of us to experience, observe, and come to our own understanding. The *Tao Te Ching,* the main text of Taoism, was written in the sixth century BCE by Lao Tsu.

The philosophy of Lao Tsu is simple: Accept what is in front of you without wanting the situation to be other than it is. Study the natural order of things and work with it rather than against it, for to try to change what is only sets up resistance. Nature provides everything without requiring payment or thanks, and provides for all without discrimination—therefore let us present the same face to everyone and treat all as equals, however they may behave. If we watch carefully, we will see that work continues more quickly and easily if we stop "trying," if we stop putting in so much extra effort, if we stop looking for results. In the clarity of a still and open mind, truth will be reflected.

—Feng, English

Taoism is based on careful observation. With practice and insight, we begin to see the patterns within nature and then understand how they may apply to our own lives. When one is in harmony with these natural laws, one enjoys ease, simplicity, and good health.

YIN AND YANG

Another philosophical underpinning of Oriental medicine is the theory of yin–yang. Yin and yang exist always in relation to one another and are used to describe the continuous and natural process of change. In Oriental medicine all things are seen as part of a whole, in relationship with all the other parts. Nothing is ever completely hot or cold, light or dark, full or empty; in other words something can only be considered hot if compared to something cooler, everything is relative to something else. There is yin within yang, and yang within yin: matter within spirit and spirit within matter, for example.

In Oriental medicine, health is understood as a state of balance, of harmonious relationship, between the yin and yang aspects of our being. Disease results when either of these forces is unbalanced, blocked, or stagnant. For example, good health demands that we balance yang activity and yin rest. This seems like common sense, yet the norm today is for us to do too much, not stopping until we collapse, or not do enough, becoming sedentary and sluggish. Both extremes leave us feeling fatigued, unhappy, unable to enjoy life, and eventually lead to illness. It is a law of nature that we live well only when the forces of yin and yang are both expressed and in harmony.

Basic Characteristics of Yin and Yang

YIN	YANG
EARTH	HEAVEN
BODY	MIND
MATTER	SPIRIT
BEING	DOING
SLOW	FAST
COLD	WARMTH
DARKNESS	LIGHT
REST	ACTION
NIGHT	DAY
FEMALE	MALE
BLOOD	QI
CONTRACTING	EXPANDING
YIELDING	FIRM

Looking at the above list, you can imagine that a yin illness may manifest with cold, weakness, slow pulse, pale complexion, and a sense of wanting to curl up in bed to rest. A yang illness may manifest with a high fever, sweating, agitation, and a rapid pulse and red face.

Most of us understand what yang activity looks like. However, the concept of yin rest warrants some exploration, as many misunderstand "rest" as merely collapsing on the couch or numbing out in some way, perhaps in front of a device with junk food.

As understood by Oriental medicine, yin is dynamic receptivity; radiant, calm being; slow, flowing restfulness. It is the soft, gentle, nourishing feminine within all beings, open to receiving as well as giving. It takes yin energy to calmly make a delicious meal and enjoy every bite of it alone or in the company of friends. It requires balanced yin to walk leisurely in the park, listening to the sounds of birds and children laughing, and feeling happy and satisfied with life. It takes this quiet yet resilient yin energy to sit still, listen, and be open to what life is waiting to give.

THE FIVE PHASES OF CHANGE

Central to the understanding of Oriental medicine is *wu hsing,* or the five phases of change. Some call these the five elements, but I prefer to call them phases of change: We are all constantly rotating in a state of flux, with the inherent capability to change. In this book, I discuss each of the five basic phases of change according to the central issues and challenges specific to that particular phase.

WOOD: Self-assertion, birth, and renewal

FIRE: Control, growth, and manifestation

EARTH: Nourishment, maturity, and transformation

METAL: Attachment, decline, and harvest

WATER: Willpower, dormancy, and storage

Each phase corresponds with particular organs, seasons, emotional states, and other attributes, as shown in the chart below. (I will be discussing the energetics of the yin organs much more so than the yang ones, as the former are more important for the purposes of this book.)

CORRESPONDENCES FOR THE FIVE PHASES OF CHANGE

PHASE OF CHANGE	EARTH	WOOD	FIRE	METAL	WATER
YIN-YANG ORGANS	Spleen Pancreas Stomach	Liver Gallbladder	Heart Small Intestine	Lung Large Intestine	Kidney Bladder
SEASON	Times of Transition	Spring	Summer	Autumn	Winter
SENSE	Taste	Sight	Speech	Smell	Hearing
ENERGY DIRECTION	Neutral	Expansion	Upward	Contraction	Downward
TISSUE	Muscles Flesh	Tendons Ligaments	Blood Vessels	Skin Mucous Membranes	Bones
CLIMATE	Dampness Humidity	Wind	Heat	Dryness	Cold
CHALLENGE	Transformation Maturity	Renewal Birth	Manifestation Growth	Harvest Decline	Storage Dormancy
BALANCED EMOTIONS	Satisfaction Gratitude	Kindness Forgiveness	Joy Love	Inspiration Hope	Calmness Equanimity
IMBALANCED EMOTIONS	Worry Obsession	Anger Frustration	Anxiety Despair	Sadness Grief	Insecurity Fear

Notice in the image below how the other phases rotate around Earth, which is in the center. The energy moves from one phase to the next, always coming back to Earth at the transitions of phases or seasons. The Earth phase helps us assimilate and transform the experiences of each phase, crucial to our preparedness and ability to successfully move on to the next phase. Earth also provides stability, which is why it is at the center of the cycle, reminding us always to return to Earth at times of transition. (In other books you may find Earth placed within the cycle of seasons rather than in the center. Both are correct, just different perspectives.)

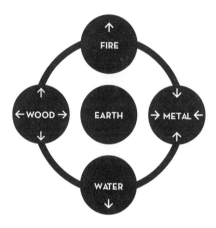

As you read about each of the five phases of change, remember that in Oriental medicine everything is part of a pattern of relationship. The correspondences associated with each phase are all interrelated, not separate ideas. For example, conditions we see in nature, such as cold, heat, dryness, humidity, and wind, also manifest within our bodies. Each of these climatic factors is associated with one of the five phases. If they are all in balanced relationship with one another, we live in a state of health. If there is excess in one, there will be corresponding deficiency in one or more of the other phases, creating symptoms and illness. A simple example: If you are too cold, you naturally balance yourself by putting on warm clothes and having a cup of hot tea (adding some ginger or brandy for extra warmth, perhaps), and soon you feel much better.

The wisdom of the five phases of change has profound implications of hope for each of us. Once you begin to observe and understand these relationships, you will be able to correct imbalances before they become serious. With this increased awareness, you will be able to live in greater harmony with life and the world around you.

> *You have to take seriously the notion that understanding the universe is your responsibility, because the only understanding of the universe that will be useful to you is your own understanding.*
>
> —Terence McKenna

EARTH PHASE
BEING CENTERED

YIN & YANG ORGANS	Spleen-Pancreas and Stomach
SEASON	Always Active (especially at times of transition)
ENERGY DIRECTION	Neutral (yin and yang balanced)
TISSUE	Flesh and Muscle
SENSE	Taste
CHALLENGE	Transformation and Maturity
BALANCED EMOTIONS	Satisfaction and Gratitude
IMBALANCED EMOTIONS	Worry and Obsession

Ancient wisdom tells us the Earth phase is the center around which the other phases and the seasons rotate. It is the foundation on which our health and wholeness is based, just as the physical earth is the ground on which we build our lives. From the earth comes our food, shelter, clothes, and fuel; our very survival depends on what the earth so generously provides for us.

Energy is neutral in the Earth phase, with a balance of yin and yang. This energy is active throughout our lives, but especially at the transitions between phases and seasons. It helps us be centered in our body, generating stability as well as transformation. Only when we have integrated this strong foundation into our way of being can we live from a place of integrity and begin to align ourselves with our true potential.

This phase is strongly connected to matter, including both the physical earth and the human body. The Latin word *mater* means both matter and mother. The body is where everything is created, grounded, and birthed in our being. The body is not a machine, indifferent to what fuels it, but rather a complex living system that needs to be respected. Everything you consume is acted upon and digested by the *qi* (pronounced "chee") of the body, a functional system that includes heat, enzymes, hormones, and all the organs working in harmony. The impurities are eliminated, and what remains has been transformed into the pure substances and energy which are the foundation for your health. However, if the body is not functioning optimally or you consume inappropriately, the energy needed for transformation to your highest potential will usually not be available.

The Earth phase is about the issues we have with food and the body, and the relationship between mother and child. These are key issues for many people I see in the clinic, especially women. Women are intimately connected to matter because of our natural capacity to create life and give birth, whether we have children or not. When Earth energy is in balance, we can access a source of abundant nourishment and use it to nurture ourselves, others, and the earth itself, simply by our awareness and presence. If we can turn our loving attention toward the body, learning to hear and respond to its needs, perhaps we can learn to love and respond to the earth in a similar way.

Yet so many of us have internalized the pervasive devaluing of matter, the feminine, and the body that we confront daily in our culture. Instead of loving and accepting the natural needs, sensations, and limitations of our bodies, many of us are constantly, if unknowingly, looking for a way out, for a way to avoid being completely embodied. We think we will be more acceptable to society or perhaps more spiritual if we barely eat at all, afraid any flesh or muscle on the body will weigh us down to the earth. Or we put on too much flesh or muscle as a way to hide, armor, or numb ourselves to the pain we feel. These extremes are contrary to the central principles of the Earth phase: moderation, satisfaction, and gratitude for all that life offers.

When you love the body, you care for it in an authentic way, and are rewarded with a sense of calm satisfaction. You can stop frantically looking outside yourself for something to satisfy your cravings, and instead be nourished by life and nourish it in return. You make a conscious choice to stop consuming indiscriminately to fill yourself up. You get to finally feel satisfied. You are enough. You have enough. The body will then give you the strength to transform all that life gives you into energy for the journey. As with most things, transformation calls for common sense and balance: enough attention to take care of your authentic needs, but not so much that you become narcissistic or hypochondriac, worried over every little thing.

CENTRAL ISSUE
NOURISHMENT

The Earth phase focuses on our attitudes around need and how to get our needs met through the nourishment we take in. Nourishment is having just enough of the right thing, the thing that will satisfy the authentic need we have in that moment. We all know how it is to find ourselves at the mall buying clothes we do not need or looking into the fridge for a treat when our authentic need is for emotional connection or intellectual engagement.

When in balance, you are able to identify and accept your needs and then use your awareness to meet those needs appropriately. Check in and ask these essential questions:

What kind of nourishment would satisfy my real need in this moment? Do I need whole food, attention, silence, movement, touch, sleep, meditation, laughter? How much is just the right amount to satisfy, not too little and not too much?

We must learn to allow for both receiving and giving. We nourish ourselves not only by consuming food and experiences, but also by contributing to the well being of our loved ones and our community. Receiving and giving are interconnected, and must be reciprocal and balanced in order to sustain us. If we reject the natural needs of the body or are incapable of receiving and fully digesting what life offers, we will not have what we need to fully experience this journey of change.

Accepting nourishment and support has been a lifelong issue for me, as it is for many people. As a young girl, I was happy to be "mother's little helper," knowing she relied on me to help out around the house and with my baby sister. But as I matured into adulthood, I started noticing a pattern in my relationships. In many situations, I was the strong one who took care of others, the one friends came to for a cooked meal or help when things were falling apart. The imbalance inherent in this pattern became clear to me one day when I mentioned to one of these friends that I, too, was having a hard time. She was surprised. "You're kidding, right? You are always so together. You don't need anyone or anything."

Her statement took my breath away. I had presented myself as completely self-reliant for so long that everyone believed this was the real me. This moment of clarity piqued my curiosity about a pattern of behavior I began to recognize in myself, and since then, have seen in so many of my patients. We use our ability to take care of others as a way to focus our attention outward and not feel our own needs. We have also learned to equate taking care of ourselves with being selfish, and so avoid it whenever possible. The result is that all too often we do not get our essential needs met, and we will eventually see this lack of nourishment manifest in symptoms.

> Allowing yourself to feel and accept your authentic needs is the first step toward receiving the nourishment available to satisfy them.

What is behind our need to nourish and give to others while not allowing them to give back? We live in a culture that also equates need with weakness. We are encouraged to do everything for ourselves, rather than rely on others or be in their debt. We idealize the concept of extreme self-reliance, of being "self-made" or "pulling yourself up by your boot straps." Women, parents, and health care practitioners are especially affected by the societal expectation of being constant nurturers and caregivers, expecting nothing in return. Like so many of my patients, I had internalized this message and was determined not to be weak.

In a broader context, unconscious attitudes reflecting imbalance in the Earth phase contribute to the current health care crisis. We do not make mature choices around the need to care for our bodies, and the result is that rates of diabetes and obesity have reached the highest levels ever seen in this country. Statistics show that more than one-third of us are obese and two-thirds are overweight. Imbalance in Earth energy contributes to the ongoing degradation of our environment as well. On a worldwide level, we have been receiving from the earth for far too long. We take all she offers so freely, feeling it is our right to waste and exhaust her resources.

By integrating the teachings of the Earth phase, we come into the natural rhythm of giving and receiving real nourishment for ourselves, our children, and our community. We can choose to grow up and allow ourselves to be aware of this truth: Our own needs and those of the earth are interconnected. We did not come into this life merely to be consumers. We have a much greater potential to fulfill, and to do so we must be in the body and really listen to what it is telling us.

EARTH IMBALANCE

- Weak digestion: nausea, poor appetite, abdominal pain, gas, bloating, loose stools
- Often tired, especially after eating
- Easily worried, obsessed, dissatisfied, with feelings of "not enough"
- Tends to have difficulty setting boundaries and staying with a regular schedule
- May be overweight or overly thin, without enough lean muscle tissue
- Symptoms worsen at times of transition, between seasons, or in damp, humid climates

BALANCED EARTH

- Healthy digestion, good appetite; feels energized after eating
- Good muscle tone and energy, healthy weight
- Able to clearly state needs and set boundaries when appropriate
- Tends to be satisfied with life and to easily nurture self and others
- Likes order and moderation; maintains a routine to get needs met
- Practical, sympathetic, and responsible

CHALLENGE
TRANSFORMATION AND MATURITY

The challenge of the Earth phase is to make mature choices to balance all forms of consumption and transform your behaviors to live with rhythmic moderation. You must learn to identify and satisfy your authentic needs for nourishment and accept reasonable limitations.

Beyond food and drink, every experience, idea, thought, and emotion is subject to a process of digestion. The ability to transform what life gives us into grist for the mill, into the substance upon which we build our character and our life, is an essential foundation for change. The transformative energy of the Earth phase helps us at all times, and especially at times of transition between the phases and seasons. The Earth phase allows us to take in the lessons of each of the phases of change, digest them, and use them for our evolution.

Almost everyone who comes into the clinic has some degree of imbalance in the Earth phase. I believe this is because we are consuming at an unprecedented level, calling on our senses to be always at work. Fast food, the Internet, and social media have given us the opportunity to conveniently and quickly consume food and content. However, as with all things, the way in which we use these resources determines whether they will have a positive or negative effect in our lives. For many of us, the virtual connection of cyberspace has left us feeling more lonely and alienated than ever before, longing for the satisfaction that comes from real-time contact with others. It is like needing a delicious home-cooked meal and the company of friends, but instead eating a microwaved dinner while watching TV alone. Technically, you have taken in calories and eaten, but you have come nowhere near to meeting your need for nourishment, and you are left wanting more.

The transformative function of the Earth phase can be overwhelmed by the constant consumption of nutrient-poor foods, information, entertainment, and stimulation. With the excessive demand on our senses, we are straining the ability of our Earth phase to transform consumption into energy for authentic growth. It is not just the quantity, but also the quality of what we take in that need concern us. We know that when we consume negative energy or "junk" in our food, relationships, or media that those substances and energies get inside us and affect who we are.

As we mature, we learn to accept the limits of what the body can do at any given moment. Limits, or boundaries, help us know where to go, what we want, and what we can and cannot do. We gradually learn to discriminate and say no to certain kinds of consumption that drain our energy, rather than enhance it. We decide every day by the quality and quantity of what we consume—media, relationships, music, images, emotions, thoughts, food, drink—what we will feel like that day, and what foundation we are building for ourselves for tomorrow. To be balanced and function optimally, the Earth phase requires moderation in our habits.

On a daily basis we need to make mature choices to balance all forms of consumption, including mental stimulation, with moderate physical exercise and rest.

Think of a two-year-old. Is it in her best interest to give her everything she impulsively screams for? Or in the case of an overextended teenager perhaps she really needs you to set reasonable limits and help her learn what she can and cannot do. Now apply this idea to your own life. Ask yourself: Do I decide to look deeply at the issue of nourishment in myself and adopt mature behaviors to transform? Or do I choose—by not changing my habits—to remain stuck in a child or adolescent stage?

To answer this question, begin by watching the choices you make around issues of nourishment and moderation, without any pressure of having to change them. At the end of the day, ask yourself, how do I feel with the choices I made today? Am I calm, satisfied, and energized? Or am I agitated, discontent, and sluggish? What do I need to feel like I have enough and that I am enough?

Becoming more conscious of the choices you make is the crucial step to beginning the process of transformation that will allow you to get centered in the Earth phase.

As we become more conscious, we begin to see that there are consequences. There are consequences to everything, and they get bigger and bigger the more we behave in ways that are not in harmony with what we know is true. This is actually a wonderful thing. It is what I call "fierce grace." It is not a soft grace; it is not the kind of grace that is beautiful and uplifting. But it is a grace nonetheless. We know that when we act from what is not true, we will only be causing ourselves pain. That knowing is a grace.

—Adyashanti

THE INTERNAL ORGANS
SPLEEN-PANCREAS AND STOMACH

The pancreas (or spleen–pancreas, as it is known in Oriental medicine) and the stomach are organs of digestion. In Western physiology, the pancreas is a narrow, six-inch long organ that lies behind the stomach, on the left side of the abdominal cavity. The pancreas is interesting because it is both an endocrine gland, producing the hormones insulin and glucagon to regulate blood sugar levels, and also an exocrine gland that secretes digestive enzymes to break down the food we consume.

In Oriental medicine, the spleen–pancreas is in charge of "transforming and transporting." It produces digestive enzymes that help us assimilate the nutrition we need for cellular function, and it provides the energy that transports nutrients where they are needed in the body. This process goes beyond food and drink to include the digestion and assimilation of all forms of information from relationships, media, emotions, and experiences into nourishment for our mental and emotional growth.

The stomach, like all the yang organs, is a hollow organ, or container. It holds food while it is mixed with enzymes and acid that continue the process of breaking down food into a usable form. This is what the classic writings refer to when they say the stomach "receives" and "rottens and ripens." Notice how this is reflected in a common expression: Those who cannot receive may say, "I can't stomach that." They cannot accept new input to be assimilated with the rest of their belief systems.

In Oriental medicine, excessive dampness is said to harm the Earth phase. Dampness results from incomplete digestion or humidity in the environment. Dampness is heavy and thick, weighing down body and mind. You may feel sluggish and tired, with edema, weight gain, or mental fogginess. Excess dampness is considered an underlying factor in yeast infections, cysts, tumors, and arthritic, painful joints.

Whatever weakens Earth and digestion will, over time, weaken the entire system. On the physical level, a weak digestive system will be unable to absorb and properly metabolize the essential minerals and other nutrients we need in order for our joints, bones, and muscles to function properly. This can lead to fatigue, pain, and disease. The physical body is the foundation for all of our growth—physical, emotional, mental, and spiritual. It is the ground of our entire being and cannot be neglected without stunting our potential on all levels.

JANET'S STORY
BLOOD-SUGAR IMBALANCE & FATIGUE

Janet is 35 years old and has an open, kind demeanor. She came to the clinic at the end of summer feeling exhausted, with mental fogginess and symptoms of poor digestion: bloating, gas, and fatigue after eating. There was a history of diabetes on both sides of her family, and she was overweight.

After her first treatment, we discussed her symptoms in the context of the Earth phase, focusing on a probable blood-sugar imbalance. "I have tried on many occasions to kick my sugar addiction, with no lasting success. Sugar has been my best friend since I was a child," Janet realized. "It helped me cope with growing up in a family where there was abuse and not much emotional support or loving kindness. Sugar has given me the sweetness I craved as a child, but now it is hurting me. If I give up sugar, I also have to address my childhood trauma and learn to nurture myself in healthy ways."

Janet typically overworked and did not eat much during the day, but overate at night, especially foods containing sugar. These are behaviors that worsen an already weakened Earth phase. I mentioned that a common manifestation of Earth imbalance is a tendency to keep moving once in motion. Janet agreed. "Yes, I noticed this summer that I couldn't stop myself from compulsively working! I worry a lot about not having enough money, even when things are really okay, so that was my excuse. I knew it was crazy, and not good for me to push so hard and not eat, but I couldn't stop myself. I just kept going all the time. Now I am exhausted."

We spoke about how familiar it was for her to be tired and just collapse on the couch with no energy to do or feel anything. Janet realized that in spite of how terrible it felt to be so tired, at least she had a good excuse to avoid experiencing her emotions and facing painful issues in her life. I helped her understand how difficult it is for someone with an Earth imbalance to identify their authentic need for regular meals and adequate rest and then make the choice to satisfy those needs. The imbalance itself takes away that choice, making us obsessive and pushing us to self-destructive extremes.

Janet committed to following these basic Earth-balancing guidelines:

- Consume mainly warm, cooked, whole foods
- Eat a breakfast that includes protein and fat every day
- Eat moderately and at regular intervals, never skipping meals
- Avoid sugar, raw and cold foods, and excess dairy, meat, and fats
- Get into a regular routine of meals, exercise, work, and rest
- Allow for moments of feeling satisfied and grateful

Janet's efforts to follow this simple program were the beginning of her redirection toward balance in the Earth phase. She went through some ups and downs and several days of reverting to old habits, combined with feeling tired and discouraged, but kept returning to the program energized and hopeful. She learned to recognize her habitual responses to uncomfortable emotions, and chose to respond differently by honing her awareness and nurturing her body with whole foods. She was eventually able to balance the emotions of Earth, transforming habitual worry and obsessiveness to feelings of satisfaction and gratitude.

Blood-Sugar Imbalances

One of the most damaging things we can do to the body is to create a blood-sugar imbalance. Since the spleen–pancreas, the internal organ of Earth, controls blood sugar through the action of the hormones insulin and glucagon, the most important change you can make for your long-term health and to balance your Earth phase is to reduce your consumption of simple carbohydrates: all forms of sugar (agave, honey, maple syrup, etc.), white rice and potatoes, processed foods, and all wheat products. I have seen patients come in one week with fatigue, insomnia, anxiety, and many other complaints, and one week later, after making this change, tell me most of their symptoms have resolved.

Eating too many simple carbohydrates is the common factor in almost every modern ailment: weight gain, inflammation, increased cardiac risk, reduced digestive function, accelerated aging, adrenal fatigue, and of course, diabetes. Today, one in two Americans is either pre-diabetic or diabetic. Diabetes is a serious and often fatal disease. The overall risk for death among people with diabetes is about double that of people who do not have diabetes.

The choices you make now will determine whether or not you end up on the path to chronic disease. And if you already have one or more of the conditions mentioned above? Believe me when I say you still have the power to significantly reduce your symptoms or completely reverse your condition in some cases. Your choices make a difference!

Too many simple carbohydrates, by the way, means too many for your body. Some people eat oodles of sugar or wheat products and seem to feel great, but do not be deceived by appearances. What we cannot see is the damage being done on a metabolic level, beginning with elevated blood sugar and mild insulin resistance that over time may develop into full-blown diabetes. This is a concern not just for overweight people. Very thin people without enough lean muscle tissue are also highly susceptible to blood-sugar imbalances, especially if they have extra fat around the belly.

What can you do? Watch how your body responds when you take refined carbohydrates completely out of your diet for one week. Observe what happens when you add some back in, and use this information when making decisions about what you eat. (See Earth Protocol for Balancing Blood Sugar in part two for more information.)

> *Foods made from wheat increase blood sugar more than nearly all other foods, including table sugar….skyrocketing blood sugar levels that rival those of a full-blown diabetic, even if you're non-diabetic.*
> —**William Davis**

SELF-ASSESSMENT
WHERE ARE YOU IN THE EARTH PHASE?

1. Do I care for and feel centered in my body?

2. Have I learned to identify and satisfy my authentic needs?

3. Is there balanced nourishment, both giving and receiving, in my life?

4. Have I found a way to contribute to my community?

5. Do I eat moderately and at regular intervals, and feel energized after eating?

6. Do I accept reasonable limits and balance all forms of consumption?

7. Do I eat a breakfast with protein and healthy fats, with little or no sugar?

8. Am I at a healthy weight, with an active body?

9. Do I cook and eat whole foods on a daily basis?

10. Do I practice moderation and experience gratitude in my life?

If you can say yes more often than no (at least 80 percent of the time) to the above questions, congratulations! You embody many of the essential qualities of balance in this phase. If not, please contemplate what needs to happen to move you toward "yes" in this phase.

Everyone contains all five phases of change, in differing degrees, so stay open to seeing yourself in each phase.

THE ONE THING
EAT WHOLE FOODS, BEGINNING WITH BREAKFAST

The most important thing you can do to balance Earth is transition to a diet of whole foods and eventually eat them every day, beginning with breakfast. Eating a balanced breakfast enables you to concentrate, make good decisions, be mentally alert and motivated, and maintain stable energy and mood throughout the day, without anxiety or depression. This sets the stage to feel clear and motivated to continue with the program when you wake up tomorrow. Yes, this one choice of what you eat in the morning can do all that!

Many people do not eat at all in the morning. They tell me they are not hungry, they do not have time, nothing appeals to them, they have never eaten breakfast and are just fine, so why change now? These excuses are signs of imbalance; having an appetite in the morning is an indication of health! Some think not eating will help them lose weight or keep them mentally alert. They suppress appetite by grabbing caffeinated drinks, not understanding that eating the right foods for breakfast is actually the best way to stimulate metabolism and support cognitive function. Some who do eat breakfast think they are doing well with yogurt, granola, orange juice, or bagels. The reality is that skipping breakfast or eating these foods high in simple carbohydrates (in other words, sugar) puts you on a metabolic roller coaster for the day, often with extreme fluctuations in blood sugar. We have become so used to this pattern we may no longer be aware of it, but the body is certainly registering the ill effects.

Are you ready to imagine a different breakfast scenario? Picture a hotel dining room filled with people surrounding a buffet table of aromatic dishes. This is my first morning in China and I am about to discover how seriously the Chinese take breakfast. Soup, dumplings, stir-fried vegetables and greens, several different kinds of congee (a soupy grain porridge), freshly made doughy bread, and garlic chicken are being heartily consumed by all present. Between bites of this delicious fare, I notice that almost everyone in the room has a healthy appetite, seems alert and awake (without coffee), and is remarkably thin, considering how much they are eating.

How to incorporate this way of eating into your own life? Eat a balanced breakfast within one hour of waking, and include protein and fat, no sugar. This will stabilize your blood sugar, energy, and mood throughout the day. This breakfast serves as a foundation that will help you make good choices for lunch and then dinner.

People who eat whole foods throughout the day, beginning with breakfast, enjoy better overall health, live longer, and are able to lose weight and maintain weight loss much more easily than those who repeatedly skip breakfast or eat too many simple carbs. You do not have to eat a lot: a boiled egg, a bite of cheese or almond butter, a handful of nuts, a protein smoothie with coconut oil and berries, a turkey roll-up. On the days you have more time or once you recover your appetite, follow the eating guidelines for the Earth phase outlined in part two of this book, and I know you will feel the good results.

> Receptivity is essential for authentic nourishment. Be open to recognizing what kind of nourishment would satisfy your need in this moment, and then allow yourself to receive it.

ADDRESSING RESISTANCE IN THE EARTH PHASE

By now, you may be thinking something like "But, but...I like sugar! I need sugar! It makes me happy!" Yes, I understand! Me too!

It is natural to like the taste of sweet. For most of us, the first food we taste is milk, in the form of breast milk or formula, and it is sweet due to the milk sugar (lactose) it contains. We deeply and unconsciously associate the sweet taste with nourishment, connection, and survival.

The flavor associated with the Earth phase is sweet. The mildly sweet flavor the earth gives us in an apple, a carrot, or brown rice strengthens the body. Sugar, wheat products, and other refined carbohydrates are overwhelmingly sweet and have powerful effects on blood glucose. Over time, these foods weaken digestive function and thus undermine the health of the entire system.

Sugar was never meant to be a big part of our daily diet. I remember speaking with a friend who is a liver transplant surgeon. He lives in Istanbul, where they make wonderful baklava, a nut and phyllo pastry literally dripping with honey. He said just a generation ago, baklava was made once a year to celebrate the abundance of the harvest. Now that it is available all year round and people eat it daily, he has seen a huge increase in swollen, inflamed livers. It is obvious to him that increased sugar consumption has contributed mightily to this increased evidence of liver disease.

We must decide to take our power back from the processed food industry that has been pushing all this junk and tricking us into believing our bodies will not know the difference. Those of us with an imbalance in the Earth phase (that is, most of us) may have difficulty integrating mature choices into a regular daily routine. Be kind to yourself and make gradual changes to incorporate whole foods into your daily diet. This will give you a truly stable foundation for your long-term health.

> When you choose to limit your consumption of sugar and other simple carbohydrates, you will feel the positive rewards very quickly: Stable energy, mood, and weight, better digestion and sleep, improved complexion and immune response, and less inflammation and pain.

PRACTICE
RHYTHMIC MODERATION

We all know how great it feels when we have enough time to go about our day without rushing. We have enough time and energy to eat when we are hungry, do the work and errands of the day, and rest when tired. This spaciousness and calm satisfaction of "enough" is the benefit of rhythmic moderation and the sign of a balanced Earth phase. We set up a regular schedule that includes all the essentials: whole food, movement, work, rest, sleep, study, play. We have a routine that allows time for everything so we do not skip meals, cancel the walk with a friend, or stay up too late working. If this does not come easily to you, begin by structuring one day per week to practice rhythmic moderation, a day during which you do not allow the demands of others to get you off track.

For several months, I had to block out times for activities in my daily appointment book to make sure I stuck with the program. It seemed silly to have to pencil "lunch," "walk," or "meditate" into my work day, but if I did not, the time would somehow get filled up with things that did not support my health. After a time, it became second nature to regularly fit in the things that were important to me. But I still have to repeatedly reassess my routine, as other, nonessential activities seem always to creep back in to take up my time, almost without my noticing.

Moderation is the key to making this work. If we think we have to exercise for two hours every day, meditate or volunteer for another two hours, meet friends for dinner and drinks, and also accommodate work and family life, well, there just is not going to be enough time. But if we accept that a brisk 30 minute walk or bike ride and another 45 minutes of quiet time or meditation is enough most days, then we will have time to eat well, work, play, and rest in the evening.

Everything in moderation—even moderation. On days off, go on the long hike you have been planning to do, dance late into the night, or spend hours cooking something special for friends. Have a great time being out of your routine! Just remember to come back to it more often than not, and you will reap the benefits of a balanced Earth phase.

GRATITUDE

The key to practicing gratitude is to be aware of what is available to you in the present moment. Even if all you can recognize is the sun shining or your breath going in and out, you can be grateful for the increased consciousness that comes from paying attention and marking the moment in your mind.

So often we focus our attention on what is wrong or what is lacking in our lives and in the world. We may develop the bad habit of complaining and treating life as a series of problems to be solved, rather than a gift to be lived. You can practice turning your attention to recognizing when you have enough and allowing yourself to feel satisfied. Acknowledge the gift of another day as you open your eyes each morning. Take a few minutes to notice the ever-changing patterns of light and clouds in the sky, the faces of the people you meet during the day, and the feeling of contentment after a good meal. When you focus on what you have in this moment rather than what is lacking, you can feel satisfied and at peace.

Experiment with feeling gratitude for your body and its connection to the earth. Sit in a place you will not be disturbed in a quiet, protected space, perhaps outside on the earth. Lie face up or down on the ground, surrendering to the pull of gravity. With your body on the ground, you will have a visceral sense of the direct relationship between your body and the earth. Feel into the substance, weight, and heaviness that is your physical body. Breathe into your belly, low into the abdomen, below the navel, and sink into the depths of your physical being-ness, into your own earthiness. You may want to speak some simple words of gratitude to your body at this time, and then listen for what your inner knowing may want to tell you.

Being able to cultivate and feel gratitude is like everything else: Practice and you will get better at it!

THE FOUR Rs OF EARTH

Use the four Rs as a guide to bring home the lessons of the Earth phase.

RECEIVE. Be open to meeting people who are balanced Earth types, who know how to prepare and eat whole foods, set clear boundaries, be satisfied and grateful, identify their needs for all kinds of nourishment, and act to get these needs met. Ask these new friends to help you learn the ways of balanced Earth. Now is the time for you to connect with the part of yourself that wants to care for yourself and others in a balanced, reciprocal manner.

REMEMBER. Your choices matter! Feeling energetic and well begins with the forms of nourishment you allow and the balance of giving and receiving in your life today. Creating lasting health takes continuous repetition over time, so please, no quick fixes or extremes. Now is the time for moderation. Use whatever tricks will work to remind you to repeat these behaviors. For example, copy and tape the Earth phase food guidelines given in part two to your fridge. Then act on the guidelines, every day, as best you can.

REFLECT. Use words like "delicious," "tasty," and "creamy," rather than "healthy," when talking to yourself and others about the food you are eating, and you will feel more satisfied. Always give yourself a choice of foods, so you feel you have control over what you are eating: veggie omelet or chicken burrito? Cheese with apples or almond butter on celery? The same goes with other choices. Reflect on your experience as you repeat the behaviors. Listen to find out what resonates with you and what does not, so you learn to recognize exactly how much and what kind of nourishment you need in the moment.

RETURN. Return to yourself, to the body, and to the Earth phase during transitions from one season or phase to the next. Take whatever time you need to digest and assimilate what you have learned here and make it your own. This is the way to lasting transformation.

The Guest House

This being human is a guest house.
Every morning is a new arrival.

A joy, a depression, a meanness,
some momentary awareness comes
as an unexpected visitor.

Welcome and entertain them all!
Even if they are a crowd of sorrows,
who violently sweep your house
empty of its furniture, still,
treat each guest honorably.
He may be clearing you out
for some new delight.

The dark thought, the shame, the malice,
meet them at the door laughing
and invite them in.

Be grateful for whoever comes,
because each has been sent
as a guide from the beyond.

—**Rumi**

WOOD
GETTING OUT
OF THE WAY

YIN AND YANG ORGANS	Liver and Gallbladder
SEASON	Spring
ENERGY DIRECTION	Expansive
TISSUE	Tendons and Ligaments
SENSE	Sight
CHALLENGE	Renewal and Birth
BALANCED EMOTIONS	Kindness and Forgiveness
IMBALANCED EMOTIONS	Anger and Frustration

When your love contracts in anger, the atmosphere itself feels threatening. But when you're expansive, no matter what the weather, you're in an open, windy field with friends.

—**Rumi**

The Wood phase corresponds to spring and is associated with renewal and birth. It gives us a chance to explore our hopes for the future and envision how we want to live, while simultaneously recognizing our relative lack of experience. When Wood is balanced, we clearly see what the next step is and feel excited and energized to plant the garden, begin a new job, or start a creative project that has been waiting to be born.

The classic texts of Oriental medicine tell us the Wood phase is powerful, forceful, and creative. Energy is expanding up and out at this time. It is the energy that compels seeds to open deep in the thawing ground, to push up and out with all their might toward the air, light, and warmth so they may grow and flourish. The life force in us follows this pattern. We feel strong energy rising from deep within us, bringing an urgent need to move, create, and begin projects based on the inner resources we have developed in other phases.

The Wood phase demonstrates how we can access a sense of inner purpose and direction in our lives. If the energy of this phase is moving freely, we are able to make plans and decisions about where we are going and how we want to get there. We move forward in our lives based on these plans, and adapt to circumstances as needed, keeping the goal in mind even when there are setbacks or delays. This is possible unless we talk ourselves out of what we want or resist what wants to come through us. A client about to turn 30 and frustrated by his lack of direction addressed this issue when I asked him if he had any hints about what might come next. "I have all kinds of ideas of what I'd like to do! But as soon as they come up, I start finding all the reasons it won't work and why I can't do it. So I don't make any new moves and can't seem to get started."

To adapt to the ever-changing conditions in our lives, we need to be flexible and yet well rooted in ourselves, much like a young sapling or bamboo stalk that naturally bends so as to not be blown over or broken by strong winds. Like the wind that corresponds with the Wood phase, the energy of spring changes quickly. One moment we contract to defend against cold, rain, and blustery winds, and then the sunshine returns and we can expand and relax.

On good days, when all is in harmony, we do not act out our anger or hopelessness on ourselves or others, nor do we move forward impulsively. Rather we wait to act until we have learned what the situation calls for on every level. However, if we have made impulsive, inappropriate decisions, or if our essential needs to create, grow, and move forward are unsuccessful for any reason, the natural flow of Wood energy will be blocked. We all know what it feels like to be frustrated. We may get tougher, push harder, or become arrogant, impatient, and irritable. At the other extreme, we may collapse at the first signs of resistance and difficulty. We give up, get depressed, and despair of ever being able to live as we had envisioned.

When life circumstances change, as they inevitably will, the Wood phase teaches us to get out of the way. We sit back and give ourselves a chance to breathe, calm the mind, and recognize any habitual reaction that wants to come up. We take a step away from the situation to gain a new perspective on what is needed now. We gather information from the body. Perhaps we are feeling frustrated and pent up because we forgot to eat, had too much caffeine, or have not exercised. Maybe we need to come up with a more effective plan, communicate more clearly what we need, or design a creative solution to meet a challenge.

According to the natural rhythm of the Wood phase, once we gain perspective, we act! The Wood phase is expansive and active, giving us the energy to move forward. We can change the habitual mental negativity of imbalanced Wood by taking appropriate action.

Until I was 28 years old, I thought of myself as a fairly easy-going person, "in the flow," with no reason to ever be angry. Looking back objectively, I was also at loose ends, without direction or purpose in my life. This situation began to shift after a particularly effective acupuncture treatment, which released an unfamiliar energy hidden just below the surface. At home after the treatment, I felt waves of powerful energy and anger move through me. I laughed at these new sensations and then cried, as memories surfaced of impulsive decisions I had made and times I had been hurt or betrayed. I noticed I was angry at myself for having been unaware and thus unable to respond appropriately in those situations.

This intense experience was unsettling but also felt surprisingly good, as if I had been shown something essential about myself and put back on track for my real life. It was a pivotal moment, brought on by the powerful energy of the Wood phase. I realized I had a choice when the energy woke up and began to move: I could continue to block it, or I could get out of its way. I was proud of myself for getting out of the way, and more than a bit awed by the power lying within me.

There is a transformative aspect to anger if we learn to use it correctly. My experience gave me a new perspective on my life as well as a sense of my inner purpose. It factored strongly in the plans I made to enroll in acupuncture college a few months later, a decision that shaped and transformed my professional life in a very positive way.

The Wood phase helps us evolve, both individually and collectively. You have to get out of the way of the natural processes of adaptation and evolution, or your growth will be stunted. Participate in the transformation by inviting in the Wood energy, paying attention to the hints and impulses that come to you from within and from the great mystery of life, and allowing something new to be born in yourself and in the world.

CENTRAL ISSUE
SELF-ASSERTION

Many of us were raised to have a negative association with the energy of self-assertion that characterizes the Wood phase. We may experience self-assertion and anger as being too edgy or harsh. We go to great lengths to diffuse anger in others and avoid it in ourselves. Perhaps there are good reasons to do so; we know the damage that can be inflicted by the inappropriate expression of anger. However, the lessons of the Wood phase demand that we learn to differentiate between excessive anger and healthy self-assertion.

Many people I see in the clinic have a particularly difficult time with self-assertion. Children learn the deepest lessons not from what adults tell them, but by observing how they act. Some of us may have learned it was better to be nice and polite, or at least to keep quiet, rather than assert ourselves to get our needs met. We thought this was normal; it was all we knew. In the natural rhythm of life, though, this is not normal at all. For example, women still earn about one-third less than men for the exact same work. Sometimes it still seems easier to behave with a goal of being liked or included than to advocate for ourselves and be called "bossy." If we avoid positive Wood energy, we may become timid and incapable of asserting ourselves on important matters, such as equal pay. Or we go to the other extreme and become arrogant and domineering, constantly at odds with others to promote our agenda.

We must learn to assert ourselves to make plans and decisions that will effectively move us toward our vision of life and through whatever is blocking our growth. If we do not, and instead repress the natural expression of Wood energy, then we also block our ability to direct our creativity and growth. Sometimes self-assertion is messy and uncomfortable, especially when we are first learning to negotiate this new terrain. But it still makes sense to learn to use it appropriately, rather than live without its power. We all know what it feels like when we manage to repress the energy of self-assertion: we become tight, tense, and unhappy! And it doesn't just go away; it is still there, unseen but building up pressure, causing resentment and all manner of troubles.

Begin your process of change by observing the small ways in which imbalanced Wood manifests in your daily life. For example, when I feel impatience arise as I wait for an elderly friend, I step back and smile at myself. Yes, once again, there is that familiar reaction! I release it and follow my breath, letting go of this violence within myself. On the other extreme, a patient I was treating for a Wood imbalance for several months told me she had finally asserted herself to speak to her family about the way they shared household chores. She said, "I couldn't put up with them expecting me to do it all, and I just told them so. The thing that surprised me is they agreed, like it was no big deal!"

It may help to think of this process as a dance with a rhythm, of say two steps back and three forward. Sometimes we need to let go of our ideas of what is right, and we step back; at other times we need to assert ourselves, and we move forward, to stay in harmony and in rhythm with ourselves and others. A balanced Wood phase will help you know the difference.

We are living at a time of great transition. Our institutions, technology, and environment are shifting in rapid, unpredictable, and often chaotic ways. You need the flexibility, rootedness, power, and creativity of the Wood phase to make the plans and decisions that will allow you to adapt to the challenges we face. Learning the appropriate use of self-assertion will help you contribute to the renewal of the world, instead of wasting your potential in senseless violence against yourself or others. Returning to the natural rhythm of self-assertion also furthers your growth as a creative and spiritual being, eventually allowing you to offer your unique talents to your community and the world.

WOOD IMBALANCE

- Inflexible, rigid, and stiff body or mental attitude
- May experience hormonal imbalance, shoulder or neck tension, headaches
- Quick to anger, frustration, negativity, or depression
- Timid and afraid to assert oneself, or too pushy and domineering
- Struggles with indecision or impulsive decision-making
- Symptoms become worse with stress, in the spring, or in windy conditions

BALANCED WOOD

- Flexible mental attitude and body, with strong tendons and easy movement
- Stable mood and energy, balanced hormones
- Sense of inner purpose; able to envision what comes next
- Adapts to change and moves forward in life
- Calmly makes plans and executes decisions after careful assessment of a situation
- Appears harmonious and in the flow of life, with little stress or tension

---

CHALLENGE
RENEWAL AND BIRTH

The challenge of the Wood phase is to be attentive and let go of any mental rigidity in order to clearly see what is ready to be born within you and in the world. Open yourself to what wants to come next, and take action to renew yourself and your purpose in life.

Spring comes and we watch the grass, trees, and flowers shoot up out of what seemed to be lifeless earth. Every spring I am delighted and surprised when this new growth appears. It seems a miracle to me that what looked dead is really alive. Yet we know this new growth did not come out of nothing; it was lying dormant in the ground waiting for the right conditions to manifest.

All five phases of change are interrelated, each supporting and enhancing the others when in balance. The phases go round and round in a cycle of rhythmic, natural change and co-creation. If we have integrated the teachings of the Earth phase we will have the energy and stability to fully assimilate and transform the experiences of the other phases to prepare us for what the Wood phase offers.

We frequently do not trust in the possibility of renewal if we are unable to see it, if it is not manifesting right now, in this moment. We think our creativity should arise out of nowhere, simply because we want it or will it. But in truth, if we have not planted the seeds within our lives and carefully tended them, or if the conditions or time are not yet right, renewal will not happen. As we come into balance in the Wood phase, we learn to watch for the signs. Do we need to pay more attention to the teachings in the other phases? Or has the mind become too attached to our own agenda, to how we think things should be, rather than seeing what the real possibilities are?

I asked a young man on the verge of college graduation if he had made plans for the future. He looked me straight in the eye and calmly stated, "I noticed how all the plans I made in college rarely turned out as I thought they would. Sometimes it was much better than anything I could have imagined, but it was never as I had planned. So I learned to make loose plans and stay open to all possibilities so I do not miss an opportunity." This is an example of the insightfulness and flexibility that comes with balanced Wood.

I am fascinated watching and learning from younger generations. So many innovative acts of creativity appear to spring naturally from them. They are coming up with new ways to work, live, travel, communicate, and contribute to their communities. It seems easy for them to create, as they are often not burdened by the rigid personal judgments, habitual responses, and cynicism that too often accompany long experience.

Similarly, balanced Wood types of all ages are fresh, flexible, and excited by visions of what is possible. They see clearly and seem to know what comes next. They create companies and design workplaces to support creativity, collaboration, and productivity. If they find they need a particular service or software that does not yet exist, they simply invent it! That is the boldness of youth, certainly, and also of the balanced Wood type. Kickstarter, Google, Facebook, Apple: All of these companies and many more have changed the way we live.

Another 20-something friend of the family told me recently, "My generation is not trying to bring down the current infrastructure or institutions, those are too entrenched. Instead, with the advanced technology we now have access to, we are developing ways to use the current infrastructure for our own purposes or bypass it altogether to create the world we envision." This is the essence of Wood speaking: "We'll bypass it altogether," like tenacious green tendrils pushing up through the cracks in the sidewalk. This is a lesson of the Wood phase: Life will not be suppressed!

Of course, nothing will ever change on a fundamental level if we keep doing things the same old, tired way or if we let physical and mental rigidity build up in our systems. Personal renewal is possible; in fact, if we do not resist life, renewal is inevitable. We can choose to shift our focus away from feelings of negativity and helplessness and turn toward finding solutions, and to the light of renewal and healing.

Fortunately, the Wood energy of renewal and creativity is not dependent on age. The potential to create is inside us all, and we can tend to it until the conditions are right for it to be born. One way to enhance your potential is to continuously return to the present moment. When Wood is balanced, you wake up every day knowing it is a new day, that you and everyone you meet have the potential to be new and full of possibility. Such an attitude keeps your eyes open to see what is really there, not what you expect to be there. Renewal is available to you if you follow the wisdom of the Wood phase.

> *To die every day to every problem, every pleasure, and
> not carry over any problem at all; so the mind remains
> tremendously attentive, active, clear.*
>
> —Jiddu Krishnamurti

THE INTERNAL ORGANS
LIVER AND GALLBLADDER

According to Western physiology, the liver is the largest glandular organ in the body and performs many vital and complex functions. It produces bile, which breaks down fats and prepares them for assimilation in the intestinal tract. It also stores glycogen, which plays an important role in blood sugar regulation. One of the major organs of detoxification, the liver filters and clears chemicals including preservatives and food additives, pesticides, lead and other heavy metals, alcohol, and drugs (prescription or otherwise). Finally, it regulates a wide variety of other biochemical reactions, including the synthesis of cholesterol and triglycerides and metabolism of the hormones estrogen and testosterone.

The liver consists of two lobes, weighs about three pounds, and is located in the upper-right portion of the abdomen. It is interesting to note that it is the only organ in the body that can regenerate itself. The ancients alluded to this when they associated the Wood phase with renewal.

The classic writings liken the liver to a general in charge of making plans and strategies. The liver is in charge of making sure the qi is flowing smoothly throughout the body. When this function of the liver is hampered, qi stagnates and a multitude of physical and emotional symptoms can occur.

Oriental medicine tells us the blood is stored in the liver when the body is at rest. If the blood is filled with toxins from overconsumption, the liver will be unable to complete its job of cleansing the blood while we sleep, and we may wake feeling tired, with a poor appetite and bad mood. This is why exercise is essential to the balanced Wood phase as movement keeps the qi and blood flowing, lessening any congestion or stagnation. We have all felt that sense of returning to a happy, harmonious mood after exerting ourselves physically.

The gallbladder is a container for the bile produced by the liver. The classics say the gallbladder is in charge of executing the plans and strategies of the liver. An excess in the gallbladder can manifest as arrogance, for example, someone who has a lot of "gall." On the other extreme, someone with a gallbladder deficiency may be timid and lack the courage to execute plans.

The essential characteristic of a balanced liver and gallbladder is harmony. There is a free, easy, smooth flow of energy, with little tension or stress in the mind or body. One of the most frequently prescribed herbal formulas in the clinic is *Xiao Yao Wan*, often called Free and Easy Wanderer, which is used to help correct liver qi stagnation and bring back the harmonious flow of qi to the system.

BARBARA'S STORY

HORMONAL IMBALANCE

Barbara is 26 years old and called the clinic in April complaining of bad PMS and a particularly severe headache. When she came in for treatment the next day, she seemed frustrated, irritable, and in a hurry to get on with her day. She told me the headaches usually came at this time every month, between ovulation and her period. The current one had come on suddenly, after an argument with her long-distance boyfriend, whom she had not seen in several months. "I feel so frustrated! My life is on hold while I wait for him to move here," she said. "So, yes, I got really angry and blamed him for how bad I felt."

I told Barbara we could talk more later, and we went directly to the treatment table. I have found it is better to first relieve tension or pain and speak after the person is more relaxed and has gained some perspective on the situation. After taking Barbara's pulses and looking at her tongue, I could tell there was heat present and an imbalance in the Wood phase. After placing the appropriate needles, I let Barbara rest.

Once I removed the acupuncture needles, Barbara said, "Most of the pressure in my head is gone and I am able to finally chill out a bit. What a relief! My PMS has been bad this month. I've been irritable, depressed, and weepy. I just can't cope with any stress before my period." I prescribed herbs for Barbara and told her I believed her headaches and PMS symptoms were signs her Wood phase was out of balance, as our hormones are mainly metabolized in the liver. I explained that diet is usually one of the root causes of Wood and hormonal imbalance.

I asked Barbara to follow these basic Wood-balancing guidelines:

- Drink fresh lemon juice in water first thing in the morning and between meals
- Add raw veggies and cooked greens to the daily diet
- Eat lightly, with fewer heavy meats and fats
- Exercise at least four times a week
- Avoid sugar, alcohol, and caffeine
- Practice taking a step back and gaining perspective before reacting to frustration

When I saw her next, she reported having had only one minor headache and said she felt more emotionally stable. "I took your advice, but I couldn't do it 100 percent every day. Even so, I can feel it has made a big difference. Exercise especially helps me feel better quickly." It took Barbara four monthly cycles of acupuncture, herbs, and consistently following the guidelines for hormonal imbalance you will find in part two for her to be free of the PMS symptoms she had experienced for six years.

I continued to see her now and then at the clinic. Sometimes she got stressed at work or frustrated with her boyfriend, who had since moved to town, and she would go out partying to blow off steam. She went through this cycle several times over the course of the following year. She kept saying, "Everyone else can have a few drinks and not have killer PMS and headaches, why not me?" and "I can't believe how stupid I am for doing this. My body just can't handle all the stress at work and then partying like I used to. I thought I knew better! Now I've wasted a whole day feeling miserable."

Each time this happened, I gently reminded her not to be too hard on herself, that it is okay to forget. We all forget, or don't want to accept limitations on our behavior. It is only human. We will do this until we decide the pain just is not worth it, or until the Wood phase is balanced and gives us the energy to move forward to the next phase of our evolution. When we are ready, the old habits that no longer serve us often slip away. Being kind and forgiving with ourselves is the first step toward this possibility. Barbara was eventually able to balance the emotions of Wood, transforming habitual anger and frustration to feelings of kindness and forgiveness for herself and others.

Hormonal Imbalance

Our hormones are metabolized for the most part in the liver. This is why complementary health care practitioners address hormonal imbalances by treating the Wood phase, often diagnosing a pattern of stagnant liver qi. This means the liver has become so congested it can no longer perform its functions of detoxifying the blood, metabolizing hormones, and insuring the harmonious flow of qi throughout the body.

Our hormones, like everything else in the body, follow a natural rhythm of daily and monthly cycles when in balance. The liver and hormones are particularly sensitive to stress and the cascading effects it has on all metabolic functions. This includes digestive stress from eating foods the body cannot fully metabolize and consuming more of a substance than the body can process, as well as emotional and environmental stresses. The many possible symptoms of hormonal imbalance that can accompany PMS, peri-menopause and menopause range from mildly uncomfortable to debilitating. Symptoms may include irritability, agitation, anxiety, depression, insomnia, mood swings, and digestive troubles.

When the body exhibits such symptoms of Wood imbalance, it is an indication that the liver is overburdened and unable to perform its many functions. This is why it is so important to reduce consumption of substances that add to the liver's load of toxins, including sugar, alcohol, and caffeine. Avoiding these substances gives the liver a needed break so it can come back into balance. (See Wood Protocol to Balance Hormones in part two for a suggested strategy for balancing hormones.)

SELF-ASSESSMENT
WHERE ARE YOU IN THE WOOD PHASE?

1. When faced with an obstacle, do I look clearly at all options and gain perspective before acting?

2. Do I make effective plans and decisions to further my life's vision?

3. Do I wake up refreshed, with a good appetite and ready for the day?

4. Do I have balanced self-assertion—neither too timid nor too pushy?

5. Is my body flexible enough to move freely and easily?

6. Are my hormones in balance, my moods and energy stable?

7. Do I have a sense of harmonious flow, without excess tension, in my life?

8. Do I engage in regular, uplifting physical activity that strengthens me?

9. Do I move congested energy through exercise, dance, art, or another method?

10. Do I practice kindness, learn from mistakes, and forgive myself and others?

If you can say yes more often than no (at least 80 percent of the time) to the above questions, congratulations! You embody many of the essential qualities of balance in this phase. If not, please contemplate what needs to happen to move you toward "yes" in this phase.

Everyone contains all five phases of change, in differing degrees, so stay open to seeing yourself in each phase.

THE ONE THING
VIGOROUS MOVEMENT

When I look back on my life, the times I have been in the harmonious flow of balanced Wood coincide with the times I was physically active. Movement and exercise increase energy, tone muscles, improve mood, reverse sluggish digestion and elimination, help release toxins through sweating, and increase oxygen flow and blood circulation. We need exercise to move blood and energy out of the liver so it does not become congested. Being sedentary tells the body it can slow down, decay, and die. Activity sends biochemical signals to the brain and body, telling them to continue to grow, heal, and live. Our bodies were built to move and to be active. If we allow the body to express its true nature, it will want to move.

If the exercise you are doing now does not significantly relieve your symptoms of Wood imbalance, you may need to undertake dietary or herbal therapy and do something more vigorous to get the congested energy to move out of the liver. Increase the resistance on your bike, walk some hills, dance longer, or find another form of exercise that works for you. You want to feel uplifted and happy after exercise, maybe slightly tired but able to continue your day. If you feel exhausted or irritable, or find you have to totally collapse after exercise, you are doing too much or the wrong type of exercise for your body.

How to begin? Take a fast walk, ride a stationary bike, go to a yoga class, swim, or simply move your arms and legs while sitting in a chair. Put on your favorite music and dance. The most effective way I have found to move out blocked energy quickly is to shake the entire body vigorously. Be sure you are in a private space and let yourself go, shaking your body in any way you want, with or without music or a solid drum beat to encourage your moves. Visualize primal and tribal dance: Stomp your feet, shake your butt, swing your arms, twirl and spin, jump up and down, shake your whole body at once. Shake until your mind is quiet and your body is at peace.

Whatever you decide to do, just be sure to move daily. Begin slowly if you don't already exercise, and build up to 30 or more minutes daily.

> The potential for renewal and new life is stored deep within you. It will manifest itself if you have prepared the ground for its birth.

ADDRESSING RESISTANCE IN THE WOOD PHASE

Your mind will come up with many reasons why you simply cannot incorporate movement into your life. The negativity that comes from imbalance in the Wood phase will tell you there is nothing you can do to help yourself. It will make you unwilling to try something new, or even to do familiar things you know work for you. Taking action to help yourself, no matter how simple or small, is the beginning of change in this pattern. If the first attempt is not quite what you need, keep at it, refining the process, until you find the most helpful exercise for you.

There are still days I tell myself I do not want to go to yoga class or get on the bike, but I have learned not to listen to this voice. On days I really resist, I say it out loud and my husband, knowing how happy I am after exercise, kindly tells me to be quiet and just do it. It is not unusual on these days for me to arrive in yoga class and grin. I know I have already done the hardest part before the class even begins: I have shown up!

A Word About Yoga

Yoga means "union." If approached with awareness, yoga is much more than a physical exercise; it is an effective way to unite body, mind, and spirit in the present moment. I encourage patients to try Iyengar, yin, or restorative yoga rather than faster-moving flow classes. Slowly coming into correct alignment and remaining in a pose long enough to observe how the mind and body are responding can be a powerful tool for transformation. It is also a way to improve flexibility, increase strength, and reduce stress.

PRACTICE
FORGIVENESS

Learning a new skill or way of being requires practice, repetition, and many mistakes. We have to relax a little bit and accept that in our inexperience, we will make mistakes. If we allow ourselves to make mistakes and learn from them, we will evolve. So we also have to learn about allowing for kindness and forgiveness, of ourselves first and then of others.

Forgiveness is not forgetting, nor does it mean you condone what you did or what was done to you. Remember and learn from the experience so that you may come to trust yourself and others again. You can rebuild a sense of trust that is based on experience and discrimination, knowing who is worthy of your trust and who is not. Forgiveness allows you to free yourself from the chains of unresolved emotion that bind you to the past or to the person who caused your pain.

Have you noticed how easy it is to make a habit of telling the story of our pain to friends, or even to people we have just met? We may believe that sharing our wounds helps to create a connection or explain who we are. It some cases this may be true, especially if we are helping others in a support group or working with a trauma therapist. However, habitual repetition often impresses the anger and pain more deeply in our minds, and we come to identify ourselves with it. Yes, certain things happened. Yet we are so much more than these negative events and experiences. After doing the practice below, consider what it would be like to give yourself the spaciousness not to have a story for a while. You might simply make a commitment not to tell the story and to resist the efforts of others to keep returning to it. You may be surprised by what this new perspective will show you about yourself.

We all know how tight and hard we get when we are stressed or when we are being overly critical, harsh, or judgmental. What works for me is to step back to gain perspective on the situation. I begin by reminding myself to come back to kindness by saying the word "soften" to myself anytime I feel myself shutting down, or when the memory of something hurtful starts to arise. This helps me let go of the inner violence and see the bigger picture in the present moment, rather than identify with the story my mind is creating from past experience. I smile to myself, relaxing my entire nervous system, as I repeat "soften," over and over. I may then experience being able to calmly stand my ground without being combative and at odds with myself and the world.

For major hurtful events, I write out the story of what happened, including all my feelings of hurt, anger, or guilt. If you try this, I suggest you write as much as you need, until you feel you have gotten it all out. It may take hours or days to complete the writing. When you are ready, you may want to take the pages and burn them in a safe place. Watch the smoke disperse and visualize the chains that bind you to the hurtful experience falling away. You may want to speak words such as "I release you. I forgive you. I am moving forward in my life."

True forgiveness is a form of kindness to yourself and others. It cannot be forced. I have found it requires our own intention as well as a certain grace that is given to us. If you find you cannot accomplish it on your own, speak with a therapist or explore nonverbal methods, such as art or dance therapy, as a way to release deeply held trauma.

Be kind, for all you meet are fighting a great battle.
—Plato

THE FOUR Rs OF THE WOOD PHASE

Here are some suggestions to help you make the most of the lessons of the Wood Phase.

RECEIVE. Be open to meeting a person who is comfortable with self-assertion and anger. I do not mean an angry person, but rather someone who knows how to use Wood energy creatively. Spend time with someone who has a sense of purpose, can see clearly what is needed in the moment, makes good decisions, and takes action to move forward in life. Observe and talk to this person about his or her experiences and insights.

REMEMBER. Remember to continually get out of the way, so new life can move through. When you feel frustrated or impatient, sit back, take a breath, and get some perspective on the situation. Do not move forward until you know what you need. Once you find your own ways to get the creative energy flowing, remember how good it feels to have a renewed sense of self, and make decisions to include these practices in your daily life.

REFLECT. Self-assertion has a natural energy meant to bring renewal to each of us and to the world. Even if you have experienced the negative side of this energy, you can now integrate the strength and flexibility of balanced Wood and learn to use it creatively. Otherwise, you risk living in the past and standing in the way of your own evolution. Reflect on your experiences of self-assertion to understand what does and does not work for you in your interactions with others.

RETURN. Return to yourself, to the body, and to the Earth phase during transitions from one season or phase to the next. Take whatever time you need to digest and assimilate what you have learned here and make it your own. This is the way to lasting transformation.

Enlightenment

Express yourself completely,
then become quiet.
Open yourself to
heaven and earth,
And be like the forces of nature:
when the wind blows,
there is only wind;
when it rains,
there is only rain;
when the clouds pass,
the sun promises to shine.
If you open yourself to insight,
you are at one with insight
and you can use it completely.
Open yourself to heaven and earth,
then trust your
natural responses;
and everything
will fall into place.

—LaoTsu

THE FIRE PHASE
EXPRESSING YOURSELF

YIN AND YANG ORGANS	Heart and Small Intestine
SEASON	Summer
ENERGY DIRECTION	Upward
TISSUE	Blood Vessels
SENSE	Speech
CHALLENGE	Manifestation and Growth
BALANCED EMOTIONS	Joy and Love
IMBALANCED EMOTIONS	Anxiety and Despair

Oriental medicine tells us that the Fire phase corresponds to summer and is the height of yang activity. The energy is now moving up toward the light of the sun and is active, expansive, and energetic. Everything in nature and within us is at its peak of expression. Fire helps us tap into our passion and gives us the energy to manifest our dreams.

The Fire phase is a time to play, laugh, and enjoy life! We delight in the long, warm days and in the simple pleasures of summer: being outdoors for hours at a time, connecting with friends, and playing with the kids. The Fire phase gives us the ability to feel more deeply in myriad ways. We communicate, express ourselves, and experience more warmth in our relationships. Fire also gives us the capacity to feel compassion. Compassion means "to suffer with." For our hearts to open, we cannot keep ourselves separate either from the suffering of others or from our own vulnerability.

The Fire phase is about our relationship to spirit, the expression of our true selves in the world, and our deep connection to life itself. Most of us consider these concepts positive aspects we would like to manifest in our lives. But how many of us believe that we are capable—or worthy—of a life lived so richly? We must be able to imagine it is possible and believe we are worthy before we will make the effort to fully engage all aspects of ourselves to act on what we know to be true.

When we look to nature we see that many plant species require fire to germinate, establish, or to reproduce. The human psyche mirrors this need for Fire to activate new life. These sparks often come from contact with the irrational or in a dream. Some years ago, I went to a Jungian therapist to address a disturbing dream I had. In the dream, I am diagnosed as having a serious problem due to impaired blood circulation from a past trauma, and told this is my last chance. The dream ends with me looking into a mirror, and instead of my own reflection, I see my mother. I was frightened by the dream and knew it was an important warning I could not ignore. It was my first meeting with the therapist, and I was giving a bit of background before telling the dream. Trying to convey a sense of acceptance about my life, I casually said, "I really don't have anything to say." I looked at this dignified, sensitive man and saw he had tears in his eyes. I was shocked by his reaction, yet curious. I later learned he was deeply hurt by the blatant falseness of my statement and my total lack of self-knowledge.

The therapist's heartfelt response made me stop and pay attention. I recognized that the image of my mother I saw in the mirror was from a time in her life when she appeared fine superficially—well dressed, hair and makeup done—right before she became quite ill. The dream was telling me I was at a similar juncture in my own life: The outward circumstances of home, work, and family reflected an image of normality and health, but danger was lurking below the surface because I was not fully living my life (represented by the impaired blood circulation). I came to understand the dream's message: This was my last chance. I had to find a way to live more authentically or I would miss the meaning of my life. What I had been feeling was not real acceptance, but rather a resigned despair as I unknowingly lived out patterns from my mother's life. I also understood that I would have to want to live my fullest potential and I would have to work for it.

This experience reminded me yet again that it is not always easy to heal the body or the soul. In order to do so, we have to sharpen our ability to perceive the deeper meanings behind outward appearances, and not believe in the false personas we often adopt unknowingly.

Of course, there is reason for negativity, cynicism, and despair in the world. But you must not succumb to these attitudes. Rather, use the consciousness the Fire phase offers to shift your attention to the tremendous love, courage, and joy available. Courage can be defined as the ability to do something that frightens you. We all feel fear. Yet you can cultivate the ability to do what is necessary anyway, despite your feelings of vulnerability. Courage (from the Latin *cor*, meaning heart) is what it takes to open the heart, follow its authentic desires for truth and meaning, and fully express yourself in the world.

> *Nature loves courage. You make the commitment and nature will respond to that commitment by removing impossible obstacles. Dream the impossible dream and the world will not grind you under, it will lift you up. This is the trick. This is what all these teachers and philosophers who really counted, who really touched the alchemical gold, this is what they understood. This is the shamanic dance in the waterfall. This is how magic is done. By hurling yourself into the abyss and discovering it's a feather bed.*
> —**Terence McKenna**

CENTRAL ISSUE
CONTROL

The Fire phase gets us in touch with our issues around love, control, and the balance between the two. The ways of love are mysterious and unpredictable. Love can sweep us off our feet and lift us up to great heights or just as easily take us to the depths of despair and leave us heartbroken. We may try to control our feelings or the other person, or twist our love into jealousy or anxiety over losing what we so desire. Some of us experience love as a deeper state that is directed toward all living beings, or even as an energy that takes us beyond ourselves to expanded consciousness. Love, in any form, has the power to evoke real transformation if we allow it to work its magic on us.

The paradox of the Fire phase is that you are asked to both surrender to be changed by love and to develop your capacity for control, engaging both heart and mind in order to reach your goals in life. You tap into your passion and let the inner knowing of the heart lead you. This inner knowing includes the irrational, dreams, and intuition. The mind follows by exerting the control and self-discipline you need to manifest your truth in the world. Many of us have tried to reverse this natural order, relying solely on intellect, analysis, or rational thought, rather than allowing the inner knowing of the heart to lead us.

Control is a word with strong associations for many of us. Younger generations often rebel against the control of their parents and the culture they were raised in. They look for ways to experience life in a new way, with more joy and meaning than simply making money or securing a position in the world. One of the most important lessons to glean from the Fire phase is that following the heart to joy and meaning actually requires quite a bit of self-discipline.

People who naturally know how to use the energy of the Fire phase follow their hearts' desires, practice self-discipline, and thereby become accomplished in their chosen endeavors. We see this with artists, writers, musicians, healers, and entrepreneurs creating new businesses and innovative products. They do not just embody the joy of self-expression, but also the exercise of control and the practice of self-discipline that is required for success.

The transition of growing fully into oneself does not necessarily come easily. We are often inadequately prepared for the challenges and responsibilities we take on, and may not trust our ability to make our dreams come true. In response, many of us overcompensate, becoming "control freaks" at home or at work, dominating and micromanaging others and the environment to gain a sense of control over our lives.

In acupuncture college, I learned the term *wu wei*, which means non-doing or inaction. When we practice wu wei, we allow life to unfold on its own. The non-doing of wu wei implies balance—neither micromanaging nor relinquishing all responsibility. Trusting life does not mean we ignore our duty. Some parents, for example, choose to let go of all control and befriend their children as though they were peers. But by refusing to accept the responsibilities of parenthood, they allow so much freedom that children are left without the discipline and guidance they need to eventually emerge wholly themselves into the larger world.

To let go of our need to over control, we have to learn to trust again. Simply stated, you have to trust life and fully embrace your vulnerability, while at the same time acting responsibly enough to meet your obligations. The wisdom of the Fire phase illuminates the need to follow the heart's desire and then to practice the self-discipline required to grow fully into who you are meant to be. You can choose to love, be vulnerable, and fully express yourself to enhance the connections you make with your loved ones and community.

FIRE IMBALANCE

- Poor circulation, red or very pale face, cold hands and feet
- Insomnia, high blood pressure, or heart palpitations
- Micromanages life or tends to relinquish all control
- Confused mind, anxiety, or despair
- Easily overheated and restless, or cold and withdrawn
- Symptoms are worse in the summer, with excess heat or stimulation

BALANCED FIRE

- Good circulation and facial color, warm hands and feet
- Healthy constitution, abundant energy
- Warm personality, capable of sustained intimacy
- Able to balance activity with restful sleep
- Mind focused, thoughts clear, full self-expression
- Joyful, enthusiastic, disciplined, with a keen sense of humor

CHALLENGE
GROWTH AND MANIFESTATION

The challenge of the Fire phase is to embrace your dreams, tap into your passion, and unite the wisdom of heart and mind to fully live your life. You must wholeheartedly want to grow, develop your consciousness, and work diligently to manifest the truth of who you are, without overdoing.

The Fire phase is a time for growth and manifestation. If we have learned the lessons of the other phases, we may now ripen into our full growth and develop our consciousness to reach maturity in every aspect of our lives. We have the physical energy to do what is necessary to fulfill our dreams, and the natural enthusiasm to enjoy the process.

It is important to look within your own heart to learn what you need to manifest in this life, rather than blindly follow whatever your family, peers, or society define as acceptable. For some, fulfillment will be about what we do, a specific career or kind of work; making money may or may not be important. For others, success may manifest in who we are and the personal relationships we have. One way is no better or worse than any other. The important thing is that you attempt to live your life as an authentic manifestation of who you are and that you honor this expression, however humble or ambitious it may be.

And the Fire phase tells you to not take yourself too seriously! One of the gifts of this phase is an opportunity to develop a keen sense of humor to balance your disciplined action in the world.

The Fire phase demands passion and the willingness to go all in to create and manifest our dreams. We all know we are much less likely to reach our goals if we are lukewarm or always hedging our bets. However, too much doing, talking, connecting, passion, or stimulating experience will burn us out very quickly. When the long, hot days of summer go on too long, crops and gardens begin to wither, water sources dry up, and wildfires blaze out of control, destroying all life in their path. The same happens within us.

There is a saying that we can only go as high as we can go deep. In Oriental medicine, this adage speaks to the dynamic relationship between the phases of Fire, the height of maximum yang, and Water, the depth of ultimate yin. As in nature, water puts out fire. As we will see later, the wisdom of the Water phase teaches us to conserve our essence and to balance being with doing to maintain our health in the long term.

The Fire phase teaches us that expanded consciousness includes everything. It warns us to be careful of the tendency of the rational mind to over identify with its verbal facility, knowledge of books, and mental concepts. Rather, you are asked to commit fully to *living* your life. To find the fulfillment you seek, you cannot stand apart from life, but rather must throw yourself into it. Think of the moth in the poet Attar's story who, intoxicated with love, hurled itself into a candle flame to show us there is no way to know love, truth, or God from the outside. You must love, get burned, find solace, and get wounded yet again. Through it all you let the rich red blood of life flow passionately in your veins, informing the way you live each moment. Only then will you truly understand the teachings of the Fire phase.

Oneness is very simple: everything is included and allowed to live according to its true nature. This is the secret that is being revealed, the opportunity that is offered. How we make use of this opportunity depends upon the degree of our participation, how much we are prepared to give ourselves to the work that needs to be done, to the freedom that needs to be lived.

—Llewellyn Vaughan-Lee

THE INTERNAL ORGANS
HEART AND SMALL INTESTINE

Ancient wisdom tells us the heart is the ruler of all the organs. If the heart is not healthy, the entire body suffers from a poor constitution and lack of overall strength. The heart is roughly the size of a large fist and is located just to the left of center in the chest. This powerful organ is in charge of circulation, pumping oxygen-rich blood to every living cell in the body.

Included in the heart's domain are the blood vessels, in keeping with the Western medical understanding of heart disease and atherosclerosis. Arteries are the vessels that carry blood rich in oxygen throughout your body. Arteries start out smooth and elastic, but become narrow and rigid when diseased, restricting blood flow to the heart. This starves the heart of oxygen and the vital nutrients it needs to pump properly. In the United States, heart disease kills more people than all cancers combined, and it claims the lives of more women than men. The good news is heart disease can often be easily prevented through the lifestyle choices we make.

The classic texts of Oriental medicine say the heart houses the mind, meaning the heart is the center of emotional and mental activity. It is in charge of memory, emotions, consciousness, thinking, spirit, and sleep. When the heart is out of balance, the spirit and consciousness have nowhere to rest. This can result in insomnia, confused thinking, rapid speech, inappropriate laughter, or mania. The essence of this concept is reflected in many common figures of speech. When we memorize something, we learn it "by heart." When we talk about feelings, we use expressions like "heartfelt," "heartless," or "warm-hearted." We get to "the heart of the matter," to what is most important, by being single-minded and consciously avoiding the many distractions that scatter our energy.

The heart also rules speech, giving us the capacity to express ourselves. We must be careful not to dissipate the heart's energy through excessive, aimless, or negative speech. The vibrations of words carry tremendous power, and we can use mindful speech as a tool to raise our consciousness.

The small intestine receives food and drink from the stomach and absorbs essential minerals and nutrients from them. According to the classics, the small intestine separates the pure from the impure, both in a physical and mental-emotional sense.

DANIEL'S STORY
INSOMNIA AND ANXIETY

Daniel showed up at the clinic without an appointment late one afternoon in July. His face was red; he was sweating and speaking very quickly, trying to get in for a treatment right away. He said he was anxious and unable to sleep well. Now 36 years old, he said this had been an issue for him on and off since his late teens.

Daniel told me he worked with computer software programs at a local high-tech company. "I work long hours, sometimes late into the evening. I have to be really on, always thinking of ways to apply the ideas I have. I like the intellectual challenge and besides, I'm making good money. But it creates a lot of anxiety for me, just having so much to do all the time."

Daniel talked the entire time as I placed the acupuncture needles, his mind very stimulated and active. I left him to rest, knowing that he would continue to talk as long as I was there. Within 10 minutes, I could hear his gentle snores from the treatment room.

After his treatment, Daniel was quiet, almost subdued. He said he was surprised by how much calmer he felt than when he had walked into the clinic. I asked him if feeling calm was unfamiliar for him, and he said, "I am just so used to talking, thinking, and being up in my head all the time. It's what I do for work, but also with my friends when we go out after work to chill."

I prescribed herbs for Daniel and asked him to follow these basic Fire-balancing guidelines:

- Eat lightly when the weather is hot, including many vegetables and fruits
- Stay hydrated, and swim or shower in cool water on hot afternoons
- Be more active during the day and more receptive in the evenings
- Reduce exposure to bright light in the evenings, and be in bed before 11:00 p.m
- Avoid the heating and stimulating effects of caffeine, alcohol, and marijuana
- Calm the heart through slow yoga, soft music, and mindful breathing

I asked Daniel to stay open to a shift from working so hard and focusing on mental stimulation to allowing times of simply being in the present moment. Daniel experimented, and over the next weeks found ways to incorporate most of my suggestions. When he followed the protocol for insomnia outlined in part two, he would sleep at least seven or eight hours most nights, but he was still very sensitive and would get thrown off when he was excessively tired or stimulated.

Weekly acupuncture treatments, herbs, and dietary changes were very effective for Daniel. He reported feeling calmer and sleeping well. Several months after his first visit to the clinic, Daniel told me he had become close to a woman he had been dating. He told me he was now finding a sense of himself in relationship to a community of like-minded friends, rather than solely in the intellectual challenges of his work. He was slowly becoming able to unite heart and mind and balance the emotions of Fire, transforming habitual anxiety into feelings of joy and connection.

If it were always summertime,
the blazing heat would burn the garden,
soil and roots, so that nothing would ever grow again.
December is grim yet kind;
Summer is laughter, and yet it burns.

—**Rumi**

Insomnia

Insomnia and poor sleep patterns are a major health issue in this country. About 50 million Americans, or more than 15 percent, are regularly deprived of sleep or suffer from some form of sleep problem. This issue does not only affect adults; many children are getting less sleep than they need for healthy development due to increased hours of homework, social media, and earlier start times in the morning.

By insomnia, I mean the many ways in which a person may not get adequate, quality sleep: inability to fall asleep or stay asleep, waking more than once in the night (possibly unable to fall back asleep), or even excessive dreaming. Many patients come to the clinic with insomnia as a major complaint. Others have gotten so accustomed to poor sleep that they do not mention it until I ask how many hours per night they sleep and if they feel rested when they wake up.

The heart needs to be calm and settled for sleep to be possible. When the heart is out of balance, insomnia may result. If the sleep deprivation is severe, irrational thinking, mania, and other mental illness is possible. A psychiatrist friend told me that in just three days without sleep the brain becomes psychotic, meaning there is loss of contact with reality and false beliefs about what is happening or who one is. This is the extreme, of course, but many of us have experienced a milder version of this reality distortion from loss of sleep.

Today, it is common for people to stay up late into the night catching up on work, watching movies, surfing the Internet, reading, and doing household chores they were too busy to get to during the day. Others cannot sleep due to hormonal imbalances and hot flashes, because they eat or drink too close to bedtime, or because they have been too sedentary during the day.

Sleep is essential to health, as it provides the yin balance to all the yang activity of the day. If you aren't getting enough sleep, your body and mind are not getting the time they need to regenerate and this may lead to more serious health issues in the future. (See Fire Protocol for Insomnia in part two for practical suggestions for dealing with sleep problems.)

WHERE ARE YOU IN THE FIRE PHASE?

1. Have I found a way to fully express myself that has meaning for me?

2. Do I have enough self-discipline to control my behavior in order to reach my goals?

3. Do I have balanced control—neither micromanaging nor relinquishing all responsibility?

4. Do I feel warmth, love, and enthusiasm in my life?

5. Is my circulation good, with warm hands and feet?

6. Do I sometimes act based on a feeling in my heart rather than solely from my rational thoughts?

7. Do I fall asleep and stay asleep most nights without difficulty?

8. Do I do yoga, meditation, or other practices to focus the energy of the heart?

9. Am I more active in the day and more quietly receptive at night?

10. Do my days include some form of play and laughter?

If you can say yes more often than no (at least 80 percent of the time) to the above questions, congratulations! You embody many of the essential qualities of balance in this phase. If not, please contemplate what needs to happen to move you toward "yes" in this phase.

Everyone contains all five phases of change, in differing degrees, so stay open to seeing yourself in each phase.

THE ONE THING
SLEEP

Most adults need seven to eight hours of uninterrupted sleep. Adolescents need more, from nine to 10 hours.

- Sleep improves your health. Consistently getting a full night's sleep enhances your immune response and lowers the risk of high blood pressure, heart disease, diabetes, and obesity. Our bodies regenerate and detoxify as we sleep, preparing us for the next day's activities.

- Adequate sleep helps with weight management. Sleep deprivation contributes to weight gain by altering hormone levels crucial to managing weight. We also eat more refined carbs and sugar to compensate for lack of sleep, causing us to gain weight.

- Sleep makes you smarter. While the body is in deep sleep, the brain works to sort out and organize information acquired during the day. This process makes sleep vital for learning, memory, and performance.

It has been only a little more than 100 years that we have had round-the-clock access to electricity in our homes, and 20 years that Internet access has been widely available. These two innovations have forever changed our lives and our relationship to the natural rhythms of day and night that had prevailed for millennia. As with everything else, this can have either positive or negative effects on our health, depending on the choices we make.

I have found it is best to follow the natural rhythm of the sun: Be active while the sun is up (the yang part of the day), and slow down and be more receptive as the sun sets (yin time). This means you may have to say no to some of the evening social activities, hobbies, or screen time you now pursue in order to re-create a routine that allows for regular, adequate, health-sustaining sleep.

Take the nights back for yin receptivity and connection, rather than give them up to yet more yang activity, work, or stimulation. Experiment a few evenings a week with getting off devices and screens by 8:00 p.m. and see what the night wants to offer you. Take some time to stretch, knit, talk with a friend, take a stroll in the neighborhood, sit outside and watch the sky, or read (not on an electronic device). Or light candles and listen to music, lie on the floor and follow your breath, let your mind wander where it will. This will calm your nervous system and help ease you into sleep.

If you find yourself staying up past 11:00 p.m. or allowing for less than seven to eight hours of uninterrupted sleep more than once or twice a week, you may need to address your tendency to focus on the mind's desires while neglecting the body's basic need to sleep, rest, and recharge. Check in with yourself and decide if this is an issue for you. If so, engage your self-discipline, read about the Earth and Water phases to better understand our need for rhythmic moderation and the wise use of resources (in this case, the mind and body), and do whatever it takes to follow the practical suggestions for insomnia outlined in part two.

Resistance is a natural part of growth. Needing to push against what is blocking your growth makes you stronger.

ADDRESSING RESISTANCE IN THE FIRE PHASE

Imbalance in the Fire phase may lead you to be too disciplined or too controlling, pushing you to finish the cleaning, the emails, the project for work, or one more post online before you go to bed. If you work full-time or are the parent of young kids and have only nighttime to devote to yourself, this gets more complicated. We tend to want more: more light, love, warmth, information, connection, or stimulation. However, once the mind is overstimulated, it is much more difficult to quiet the nervous system and ease into a restful sleep. If you want to get back into healthy sleep patterns, you may need to accept that for now, you just cannot do it all.

The other side of this imbalance is failing to adequately engage your own self-discipline, allowing yourself to stay up late mindlessly surfing the Internet or pursuing other unnecessary activity. We need to establish routines and follow through with them on a regular basis to correct chronic sleep problems.

Changing your habitual behavior may not come quickly or easily, so not to worry if you feel a little uncomfortable or anxious as you practice these quiet, receptive evenings. Discomfort does not mean you should give up! Simply acknowledge you are in unfamiliar territory and let yourself be curious about what will support you to gradually ease into it over time.

PRACTICE
PLAY

We all know that children are happier and calmer when they can run around outdoors. Research now shows that they have more mental clarity and are less stressed if they can play hard, indoors or outside. But play is not just for kids; we all need the benefits of play! Today the average American spends less than an hour in unstructured outdoor play and more than seven hours in front of an electronic screen each day. We have lost our connection to the natural world and to the joys of play, and are out of shape and stressed out as a result.

I spent countless hours playing outdoors as a child. We rode bikes, climbed trees, ran races, and played kick-the-can until parents called us in to dinner. There were summer days when all I did was play outside, from the moment I woke until bedtime, with brief pit stops for food and perhaps a board game if it was really hot. I remember laughing, feeling connected to my friends and the neighborhood, enjoying school, and feeling relaxed and very happy for most of my early childhood.

As adults, we need to restore a sense of play both at work and at home. Many of us are working longer hours, eventually becoming overwhelmed and burning out. We seem to forget that success at work depends more upon the quality of work we do than the amount of time we put in. The more balanced we are, the better for everyone. Certain high-tech companies have this figured out, offering their employees play areas, ladders connecting floors, treadmills at desks, and walls to scribble notes on. Most of us can get similar benefits by simply walking outside for a few minutes, shooting some hoops set up in the break room, or talking and sharing a few laughs with our colleagues during the day.

Play helps us connect, encourages teamwork, increases energy, reduces stress, and refreshes the mind to help us see problems in a new way. And it's fun! We open up to life and expand our consciousness when we are having fun and laughing. Play out in nature and inside; play music, sports, cards, and board games; dance; be silly; watch comedies; and connect with friends over a shared meal or activity you enjoy. Look for your own unique ways to put the play back in your life, and do it as often as you can.

THE FOUR Rs OF THE FIRE PHASE

The following suggestions are meant to help you internalize the lessons of the Fire phase.

RECEIVE. Be open to the energy of love helping you on your path. Look for a book, practice, or person who can support you in expressing yourself and engaging your passion for life. Befriend a balanced Fire type who is living his or her dream with self-discipline and responsibility, as well as joy and laughter. Look for ways to come into relationship with the inner knowing of your own heart.

REMEMBER. Remember to engage your self-discipline and get into a rhythmic cycle of being more active during the day and in the summer, when yang energy is stronger, balanced by more rest during the evenings, night, and winter, when yin energy dominates. Balance the activity of the Fire phase with practices that focus the energy of the heart: yoga, meditation, music, or devotional chanting. Repeat the behaviors and practices of the Fire phase until they come naturally to you.

REFLECT. Reflect on what resonates for you, and what does not, in the way you currently relate to life. Perhaps it is time for your habitual attitude of either being too cold, withdrawn, and controlling or too warm, expansive, and without limits to come into balance. Imagine being in love with all of life rather than one individual, and experiment with love expressed in new ways that are not centered solely around control, anxiety, or the self.

RETURN. Return to yourself, the body, and the Earth phase during transitions from one season or phase to the next. Take whatever time you need to digest and assimilate what you have learned here and make it your own. This is the way to lasting transformation.

THE METAL PHASE
KNOWING YOUR VALUE

YIN AND YANG ORGANS	Lung and Large Intestine
SEASON	Autumn
ENERGY DIRECTION	Contractive
TISSUE	Skin and Mucous Membranes
SENSE	Smell
CHALLENGE	Harvest and Decline
BALANCED EMOTIONS	Inspiration and Hope
IMBALANCED EMOTIONS	Sadness and Grief

*Why are you so enchanted by this world, when a mine of
gold lies within you?*

—Rumi

Metal represents our relationship to inner value, structure, authority,
and the connection between father and child. The Chinese word *jin*
is used for the Metal element, and it translates as the metal gold. It is
the gold, the inner treasure within each of us, that we must uncover
in this phase. We turn our attention inward to access our values and
what our unique inner knowing wants to teach us. By values I mean
the qualities that define who you are at the center of your being and
the things that have to be a part of the way you live for you to be
fulfilled. Reflecting on what you love, what inspires you, and what you
spend time and money on will give you a clear idea of your values.

The ancient wisdom of Oriental medicine tells us that the Metal
phase corresponds with autumn, a time of harvest and decline. This
is a time to reap the abundance of the expansive, energetic work of
the Wood and Fire phases. Yet there is often a sense of melancholy
at this time that may seem unrelated to anything happening in our
outer lives. Patients come into the clinic saying they feel sad "for
no reason." How interesting that 2,000 years ago, those compiling
the classic writings stated that Metal relates to grief, melancholy,
and sadness. I remind my patients that these feelings are part of
the natural cycle. The shorter, darker days of autumn may touch a
longing within us for something we cannot quite name, or remind
us on an unconscious level of a loss of connection to someone or
something we valued very much.

In Taoist cosmology, the human being is the union of heaven and
earth. The heavenly influence is said to come through the lungs,
from the inspiration of pure, clear energy. Thus, the simple act of
breathing gives us both physical energy from oxygen and inspiration
from a divine source to use in our daily activities. One of the gifts of
the Metal phase is to be inspired by the beauty in music, art, nature,
and people. Inspiration comes from the beauty of ordinary things as
well, and from moments of clarity when we see things as they really are.

A friend told me about a time he could not figure out how to design a small cottage he wanted to build on his land. After taking a long hike, when his lungs were wide open from the exertion, he sat quietly on the land to rest. Suddenly, he saw exactly how to design and place the house on the land.

Metal is also the sharp-edged knife that allows you to cut to the core, giving you the ability to discern what is useful and the strength to cut away what is not. When balanced, you can determine who is truly worthy of your respect before allowing their authority to influence you. You are open to relationships, teachers, ideas, and leaders who will influence you in ways that further your growth. The strength of the Metal phase helps you to know your own value, so you are able to both be enriched by true authority and walk away from anyone who attempts to diminish you.

In the Metal phase, energy is contracting and moving inward both in nature and within us, supporting our capacity for inner reflection. The Metal phase is when we transition from the expansive, yang energy of summer into the cooler, more inward, yin energy of autumn. Human bodies and psyches unconsciously respond to this time of contraction and prepare to go even deeper as winter approaches. We are reminded to start to retreat within and reflect on life's happenings, so that when spring comes, we are ready for action, ready to sprout and grow into the next phase of our evolution.

For many of us, inward reflection is unfamiliar, perhaps even scary and uncomfortable. Our extroverted culture tells us to seek external stimulation and activity, to be always emotionally up and on. The seemingly solid ground of youth and outward expression are what this culture encourages and rewards, not the attitude of reflecting on the inner world. We may perceive our inwardness in the Metal phase as depression, when in reality we are simply following the natural movement of energy inward at this time.

This process described in the Metal phase can happen at anytime in a person's life, so younger readers, please stay with me here. You may be approaching this phase consciously for the first time in your life due to a loss, an illness, or a longing for something that is calling you inward. The ancient wisdom applies to each of us, as we go through all of these phases many times before we reach the actual physical autumn of our lives.

> *Japanese master Nan-in received a university professor who came to inquire about Zen.*
>
> *Nan-in served tea. He poured his visitor's cup full, and then kept on pouring.*
>
> *The professor watched the overflow until he no longer could restrain himself. "It is overfull. No more will go in!"*
>
> *"Like this cup," Nan-in said, "you are full of your own opinions and speculations. How can I show you Zen unless you first empty your cup?"*
>
> —Reps, Senzaki

CENTRAL ISSUE
ATTACHMENT

The Metal phase is about the inhaling and exhaling of life. We consciously inhale, take in, and accept what life offers—joy, sorrow, birth, death—and from all this experience we forge our inner values and claim our dignity as human beings. We must also consciously exhale and let go of all that is no longer available to us or contributing to our evolution. Common sense tells us there can be no in breath without an out breath.

Oriental medicine teaches us that the Metal phase reflects our issues around attachment. When Metal is in balance, we have the capacity to become deeply attached to and enriched by what we deem valuable—a person, principle, career, or practice. And at the same time, Metal helps us discriminate and know what no longer furthers our growth and gives us the strength to grieve important losses and let them go.

I recently attended a memorial service for a loved one who died at the age of 27. The sense of loss was immense, and many of those closest to her could not accept that we had lost her. We wanted to honor her and did so by telling stories of her life and the ways she was special to us. Our attachment to her had enriched our lives and brought us so much joy. Now that attachment was breaking our hearts.

It seemed so natural to be in the midst of this circle of friends and family that at first I did not see what made this event unique in my experience. All of these people were there because of how the young woman had lived her life—with extended and meaningful connections to family, friends, church, work, and neighborhood. She did not own much, did not make much money, but was a truly alive, generous, and happy person. She had valued each person there and we were now openly grieving her loss.

Only days before attending the memorial, I had an opportunity to hear Frank Ostaseski speak about spirituality in dying. Through his work with hospice and the Metta Institute, Frank has been with hundreds of people through the dying process. Something he said really resonated with me. In his considerable experience, as we approach death, there are two basic questions that come up: Am I loved? Have I loved well? Another way to phrase this, which adds understanding for me, is: Am I valued? Have I added value to another or to the world? With our last breaths, we want to know if our lives have had meaning and value.

These are essential questions to ask, and not only when we experience loss or when death is near. For who knows when that time will come? It certainly is not as predictable as most of us would like to believe. If we accept the common sense truth that life is impermanent, rather than busy ourselves resisting it, we would have the opportunity to use our precious time to reflect on our values and how we can live them more faithfully each day.

We have all been inspired by someone who feels passionately about another person, a career, an issue, or the expression of beauty in the world. And yet other people choose, unconsciously for the most part, to remain somewhat detached from life to avoid the inevitable pain that comes with fully loving someone or something in this world. Balanced attachment allows us to hold on to what is of value to us and let go of what no longer furthers our growth when the time comes or when circumstances demand it, as in the case of death.

But what is valuable? All too often in our materialistic culture, inner value is overshadowed by outer values. Whatever our particular peer group values becomes our standard for judging them and ourselves. Do we have the right job, clothes, devices, music, and gear? Enough money, friends, talent, brains, and love?

My patients tell me how tired they are of being judged for how they look and what they consume rather than for who they are. This is the sad reality for anyone who is judged to be too thin, too fat, too poor, too ill, or too tired to play the game—or for those of us who judge ourselves. Have you noticed that fighting against the natural rhythms of life is a losing battle? What if we could accept our place in the rhythms of change and clearly see that the totality of our experience, the failures as well as the successes, the contraction and the expansion, has brought us to this moment with its potential for wholeness?

By following the wisdom of the Metal phase, you return to the natural rhythm of inward reflection that leads you to know and value what is truly important and let go of everything else. Now you can be inspired by the clear energy from the heavens and access your authentic strength, the real gold, within yourself.

METAL IMBALANCE

- Shortness of breath, respiratory allergies, or skin rashes
- Dry skin and mucous membranes
- Frequent and lingering illness, such as colds, coughs, sore throats
- Excessive grief and melancholy

- Disorganized, unable to keep commitments, sedentary
- Symptoms usually worsen in autumn or in dry climates

BALANCED METAL

- Balanced attachment, knowing when to hold on and when to let go
- Moist, supple skin and mucous membranes
- Strong immune system, seldom ill or recovering quickly
- Physically active, with strong lungs and voice
- Grieves deeply and completely before letting go
- Reflects inwardly; inspired by beauty in many forms
- Strong, discriminating, principled, living by inner values

CHALLENGE
HARVEST AND DECLINE

The challenge of the Metal phase is to open to inspiration and harvest what is valuable in your life. Let go of what no longer furthers your growth and develop the strength to grieve important losses. Set your focus on wholeness, looking beyond superficial appearances to connect more deeply to life and spirit.

Anyone, at any age, may find herself or himself in the Metal phase. It is the harvest time of reaping abundance; we may feel inspired and deeply connected to self, the world, and spirit, seeing the beauty in people, art, music, and nature. It is also the time of decline; we may want to give up on life, feeling hopeless and unable to think of anything worth living for. We have all seen how the latter situation may come about after the loss of a loved one or due to an accident or an illness, when the physical strength we have relied upon is diminished and our defenses are broken down. We tend to think of the harvest as "positive" and the decline as "negative" (and something to avoid), but both are necessary for the journey.

The ancient wisdom of all spiritual traditions is founded on the inclusion of everything in life. We cannot have day without night, love without tears, a body without decline, or an in breath without an out breath. It is foolish to believe and behave otherwise. Harvest and decline are not separate from each other, but rather equal parts of life's wholeness.

In autumn, the days are shorter and the light weaker, leaves are falling, and plants are dying or going dormant for the upcoming winter. In the phases of a person's life, Metal is the time of old age. Our culture still holds a deep-seated belief that after a certain point, age 50, 60, or 70, there is not much left of value within us or for us in life. Even if we stay healthy and engaged with life as we age, the body naturally slows down and we have to accept more limits on our physical activity.

At any age, we feel less in control in the Metal phase due to the natural contraction occurring at this time or the losses we have suffered. Losing your loved ones, sense of identity, or control over the body is no easy thing, and minimizing the difficulty does not help. However, if approached with awareness, you may see that in a larger context, loss of any kind can be accompanied by—or in some cases is the prerequisite for— the grace of your surrender to the wholeness of life. You can choose to shift your focus and look toward a more expansive spiritual understanding, rather than get stuck in regret for the physical decline and contraction of the body. This takes tremendous inner strength, the kind of strength a balanced Metal phase gives you.

Eternity

He who binds to himself a joy
Does the winged life destroy;
But he who kisses the joy as it flies
Lives in eternity's sun rise.

—William Blake

LUNGS AND LARGE INTESTINE

The lungs are in charge of respiration. These vital organs fill the chest cavity and make up most of the lower respiratory tract. Their most important job is providing oxygen to capillaries so they can oxygenate blood and remove carbon dioxide.

The classic texts tell us that through breathing in—inspiration—we take in *qing qi* (pronounced "ching chee"), the clear, pure energy that is depicted in metaphors as coming from the heavens. Thus, the simple act of breathing in gives us physical energy from oxygen as well as inspiration from a heavenly source. In Oriental medicine, the lungs are also in charge of our body's defense or immune mechanism, what is called protective energy, or *wei qi*.

The large intestine, or colon, receives the mostly digested food from the small intestine and absorbs excess water, creating the stool. The large intestine is referred to in the classic texts as "the great eliminator," responsible for the elimination of all digestive waste.

The process of elimination also encompasses mental and emotional waste. A Metal dysfunction may cause us to hold onto emotions, ideas, and principles long past the time they have any worth for our development. This constipation of the mind can keep us tied to detrimental thought patterns and take up all available mental space, leaving no room for anything new and essential to come into our life.

CHRONIC SINUS INFECTION

Susan is a 42-year-old woman who came to the acupuncture clinic at the height of the Metal season, suffering from yet another sinus infection. She told me she had been getting an infection every autumn. She was pale, had a weak voice and shallow breathing, and complained of exhaustion, mild depression, and constipation. Susan had used antibiotics for sinus infections in the past, but now felt inspired to try something different.

When I asked her about the onset of her symptoms, she told me her father had died in October four years earlier and she had gotten the first sinus infection soon afterwards. Susan explained, "My relationship with my dad was mixed. When I was young I thought he was the smartest man around and I loved being with him. He left when I was nine and I was really angry at him, but mainly sad. We weren't very close when he died, and I have regretted that very much."

Oriental medicine tells us that unresolved grief weakens the respiratory system, which includes the sinus and nasal passages. My experience with Hakomi, a body-centered psychotherapy, has shown me how we tend to move our attention away from a place in the body that hurts. We effectively seal off the hurt place, avoiding it and the pain it contains, hoping it will get better by itself. But how can it get better if deprived of energy, oxygen, and our awareness? What if we were to stop avoiding pain and instead do the opposite, bringing our energy back to the area that is calling out for attention? I noticed the sadness in Susan's voice when she spoke of her father, so I began the treatment with a few minutes of massage on her upper back to bring energy to the part of the body that houses the lungs and heart. I then needled acupuncture points to balance the physical energy of the lungs, as well as points corresponding to the emotional aspects of sadness and grief.

I mentioned to Susan the possible connection between her unresolved grief and the sinus infection. I suggested her grief was a sign of how much she valued her relationship with her father and asked her to consider holding onto her love for him while at the same time letting go of her regrets. I left her to rest quietly.

After the treatment, she said, "I could really feel the grief of losing my dad. I was surprised at how fast the tears came. I thought I was over all that. I began to have memories of us together, how kind he was and how sad he was, so alone. In my chest I could feel this love for him, and the sadness, all at the same time, and somehow it seemed okay."

I asked Susan to follow these basic guidelines to help balance Metal:

- Eat cooked, warm, moisture-filled vegetables, soups, and stews
- Moisten the diet by cooking with coconut oil or ghee; add coconut oil to hot tea
- Get mild exercise in the fresh air, and get enough rest
- Run a humidifier to keep airways moist
- Avoid cold drinks, cold and raw foods, greasy foods, sugar, dairy, and wheat
- Use journaling to explore memories, feelings, and thoughts

Three weeks after her initial treatment, Susan realized she had never let herself go to the bottom of her grief over her father's death. Before, when she felt the sadness coming on, she would find a way to shut it down by distracting herself or numbing her feelings. She had not been able to resolve the sadness because she had not fully experienced it. Susan consciously chose to turn toward the sadness and allow it to teach her about her inner world. She felt hopeful now that her health would improve through acupuncture, herbs, dietary changes, and the increased awareness of her inner process she had gained by journaling every day.

With a few follow-up treatments and continued exploration through journaling, Susan was able to heal both her physical condition and her unresolved grief. She has not had another sinus infection since. Eventually, she was able to fully balance the emotions of Metal, transforming habitual sadness and grief to feelings of hope and inspiration.

It takes strength to feel your pain and the pain of others. But to be a whole human being, you must feel pain as well as joy. Paradoxically, when you allow yourself to fully feel the depth of your own sorrow and the pain of the world, you can then be filled with the immense joy of being alive.

Lowered Immune Response, Constipation

A dry climate will weaken the mucous membranes of the lungs and large intestine and impair one of their important functions: that of sloughing off bacteria and allergens from the system before they have a chance to create illness. This is common where I live in the Southwest, where the climate is often extremely dry. Autumn comes, and we have weeks or even months with no precipitation at all. The cold winds begin to blow, dry leaves fall, and the air is filled with dust and other allergens. People stay inside more, getting less fresh air and exercise, and I see many more patients with seasonal allergies, colds, and flus in the clinic.

Getting the occasional cold is not a problem; this may be a natural way to get you to slow down for a few days and allow the body to eliminate toxins. When colds become chronic (occurring more than once or twice a year), this is an indication the immune system is not functioning optimally and it is time to address the underlying causes before serious illness develops. Often this means focusing on a possible Metal imbalance and correcting it with acupuncture, herbs, and dietary therapy.

One reason Metal phase imbalances are so common is our increasingly sedentary lifestyle. When we are not active on a regular basis, our respiration and elimination suffer. Activity causes us to breathe deeply, generating vital qi to strengthen the lungs and large intestine. When we are active, we stimulate movement through the entire body, strengthening and balancing respiration and elimination (See Metal protocols in part two for advice on treating constipation and improving immune response.)

WHERE ARE YOU IN THE METAL PHASE?

1. Do I feel valued?

2. Have I added value to another's life or to the world?

3. Am I deeply connected to life and able to let go when necessary?

4. Am I organized, principled, and able to keep my commitments?

5. Do I allow myself to fully feel grief and sadness when they arise?

6. Am I physically active, with strong respiratory and immune function?

7. Do I consume water and healthy oils to provide essential moisture?

8. Do I practice mindful breathing?

9. Do I find inspiration in art, nature, music, relationship, or other ways?

10. Do I journal and acknowledge the beauty in everyday moments?

If you can say yes more often than no (at least 80 percent of the time) to the above questions, congratulations! You embody many of the essential qualities of balance in this phase. If not, please contemplate what needs to happen to move you toward "yes" in this phase.

Everyone contains all five phases of change, in differing degrees, so stay open to seeing yourself in each phase.

THE ONE THING
MINDFUL BREATHING

Breathing in and out is a simple act we do automatically, without thinking. We inhale fresh air full of oxygen and vital energy; we exhale the waste products. It is easy to see how the process of breathing relates to the Metal phase: We take in what is valuable and we let go of what is not.

Mindful breathing is the fundamental practice for the Metal phase. It strengthens the lungs, increases energy, reduces stress, and improves immune system function. The breath is also our connection between mind and body. Breath ties us to the present moment, the only one that holds any potential for change. Noticing the breath helps us to stay here in this moment, neither losing ourselves in remembering the past nor worrying about the future.

How to practice? Simply follow the breath with your awareness, in and out. Breathe into the belly, allowing it to rise. Pause. Breathe out and let the belly deflate. Pause. Repeat many times, in a slow and relaxed way, never rushed. When you get distracted, gently bring your awareness back to the breath, in and out. Do not worry if you can sit still for only a few minutes at a time. That is a good start. You can also do walking practice. Walk slowly, mindfully, taking one step with the in breath, one step with the out breath.

You can practice anywhere, anytime. Buying groceries, doing the dishes, driving the car, taking a walk, lying in bed unable to sleep, while feeling annoyed or rushed: Simply remember to bring yourself back to the breath and back to being fully present. Being fully present is what allows us to see the beauty available in every moment. We see the face of the cashier at the grocery store, the small flower growing out of the sidewalk; we feel the gentle breeze on our face. These are the small moments that connect us to life, to its beauty and its impermanence, moments we miss when our minds are preoccupied with a thousand other things.

I like to practice mindful breathing when I am alone and know I will not be disturbed by the phone or other people. I prefer to practice first thing in the morning or before bed, but any time you can carve out for yourself in a quiet place is worthwhile. Allow yourself to breathe, in and out, and feel your connection to yourself through this simple yet profound practice.

If your mind needs a guide during mindful breathing practice, try this meditation from *Being Peace* by Zen author and teacher Thich Nhat Hanh.

"Breathing in, I calm my body.

Breathing out, I smile.

Dwelling in the present moment

I know this is a wonderful moment."

This can be shortened, one word with the inhalation, the next with the exhalation.

"Inhale: Calming

Exhale: Smiling

Inhale: Present moment

Exhale: Wonderful moment."

Words are powerful. When we say, "I calm my body" we can feel the body calming. Really smile while breathing out. A smile will relax the muscles of the face as well as the entire nervous system. The act of smiling (whether you feel like it or not) tells your body you are okay, you are safe, you can relax.

Getting rid of unnecessary accumulation and simplifying your life strengthens the Metal phase. Mindful breathing is as simple and powerful as it gets!

ADDRESSING RESISTANCE IN THE METAL PHASE

Those of us with an imbalance in this phase may notice resistance on two levels. If our lungs or immune system are compromised, we may be frequently ill or simply lack the energy to make the effort necessary to strengthen the body. We may think it is easier to take prescription medications, something to help us feel better quickly. Sometimes we do need such substances to heal our bodies, and we must use our discrimination or get professional advice to decide what is appropriate.

Hope and inspiration are the positive emotions of the balanced Metal phase. With imbalance, when we are ill or feel emotionally weary, we may have difficulty believing there is value in something as simple as breathing. We may be tempted to give up before we even begin. At one time, I was dismissive of the subtle power of the breath, as though I had chosen to take up less space in my body and the world by breathing shallowly. Refusing to consciously acknowledge this act that is essential to our very survival is one way to diminish our own value.

Remember, the simple act of breathing gives us physical energy from oxygen, as well as inspiration from a heavenly or divine source to use in our daily activities and for our healing. To breath with awareness increases its power.

PRACTICE
JOURNALING

Journaling is a powerful technique for inner reflection. It can be very helpful in reconnecting you to your self and your own inner knowing.

In a quiet place where you will be undisturbed, close your eyes and breathe into your belly. Feel into yourself and remember who you are. Literally re-member, bringing all the pieces of your self back together. Come back to this moment, to this breath, to this life. Now you are ready to begin.

Journaling is simple. Simply get pen and paper (or your computer) and start writing about whatever is on your mind. Write a page or two, not worrying about grammar or form. Just get your thoughts and feelings out. Write down whatever comes to mind—dreams, thoughts, reactions, feelings, jokes, poems, quotes you respond to (either in a positive or negative way)—each has something to teach you.

What beauty inspires you in simple moments, objects, people, and the world? What awakens the deep longing within you? Look for it and allow yourself to be touched by what presents itself to you. Observe yourself and your reactions to the behaviors and comments of others, especially to the things that disturb, irritate, or anger you. These can lead you to a deeper understanding of yourself. Instead of believing what your mind habitually tells you about the other person or the situation, get curious. Ask yourself: Why is this so disturbing to me?

Writing frequently, even daily, will help you gain perspective and begin to recognize patterns in your life. Ten minutes a day is enough time to keep the practice going and to stay in touch with yourself. The writing doesn't have to be pretty or nice—in fact, if it is, be suspicious! This is not the time to seek anyone's approval or try to please; it is a time for honesty, awareness, and acceptance of what is true in your life. Your journal will be kept private, for your eyes only, so tell yourself the truth. You may be surprised by what is in there.

THE FOUR Rs OF METAL

The following suggestions are meant to help you internalize the lessons of the Metal phase.

RECEIVE. Look around you for inspiration—in a person, art, music, or nature. Be open to meeting a balanced Metal type who lives their values, aims for wholeness in life, is not caught in superficial appearances, and is connected to spirit. Look for what makes you smile, cry, laugh, or feel longing. That is where you want to focus your attention!

REMEMBER. It is up to you to discriminate among all possible options and decide what you need, what will be of value, for the next stage of your growth. Is your Metal phase asking you to strengthen your immune system through acupuncture, exercise, and dietary therapy? Getting organized and making a commitment will engage your underlying strength to implement what works for you.

REFLECT. What do you value at this time in your life, and what is now nonessential? Let go of things, tasks, and roles you have played that no longer interest or serve you. Allow those unwanted attachments to fall away, while holding on to what has authentic value. Reflect on what resonates with you in the behaviors and practices that strengthen Metal.

RETURN. Return to the Earth phase during transitions from one season or phase to the next. Take whatever time you need to digest and assimilate what you have learned here and make it your own. This is the way to lasting transformation.

The Buddha's Five Remembrances

I am of the nature to grow old. There is no way to escape growing old.

I am of the nature to have ill health. There is no way to escape having ill health.

I am of the nature to die. There is no way to escape death.

All that is dear to me and everyone I love are of the nature to change. There is no way to escape being separated from them.

My actions are my only true belongings. I cannot escape the consequences of my actions. My actions are the ground on which I stand.

—**Buddha**

THE WATER PHASE
DIVING DEEPLY

YIN AND YANG ORGANS	Kidney and Bladder
SEASON	Winter
ENERGY DIRECTION	Downward
TISSUE	Bones
SENSE	Hearing
CHALLENGE	Storage and Dormancy
BALANCED EMOTIONS	Calmness and Equanimity
IMBALANCED EMOTIONS	Insecurity and Fear

You've been walking the ocean's edge,
holding up your robes to keep them dry.
You must dive naked under and deeper under,
a thousand times deeper! Love flows down.
The ground submits to the sky and suffers what comes.
Tell me, is the earth worse for giving in like that?

—**Rumi**

Water is the source of life on this planet and within our own bodies, nourishing and cleansing us on the deepest levels. In Oriental medicine, the Water phase is the root of all energies of the body and of the deep essence, *jing,* that determines our vitality, resistance to disease, and longevity. There is no way to overemphasize the importance of the Water phase, as it represents the stored potential of our entire lifetime.

Water corresponds to winter, a time in nature of increased cold, darkness, and silence. This part of the year can be a gentle, nurturing time of stillness. Think of snow quietly falling on fields lying fallow, animals hibernating. The natural world slows down, rests, and waits. In nature and within us, winter is a time to store our physical energy and wisely manage resources (food, fuel, energy) in order to survive and have the strength necessary for the next phase, spring and renewal.

Water is the phase of ultimate yin, with the energy moving down. This energy is tied to the deepest essence of the body, the marrow in our bones, the root of our being. The Water phase reflects our relationship to the unconscious mind, sexuality, power, financial resources, and the unknown. For many of us, these are challenging issues, to say the least. We may be intrigued by what lies within us, but afraid of what may bubble up from the depths through dreams, memories, and images. We may spend considerable time and energy staying busy and engaged in myriad pursuits, avoiding the Water phase and the most profound parts of ourselves.

As well as this deep stillness, there is immense power in the Water phase. Imagine a river after heavy rain. The water moves swiftly, changing its course to flow around massive boulders, downed trees, and other obstacles. If the water has been dammed up or the rains prolonged, it may break through and flood, carrying away everything in its path, leaving only devastation. Think of the images we see of super storms, typhoons, hurricanes, and tsunamis.

The good news is that there is a wellspring of both wisdom and power within us if we dive into our psyche to access it. I have spiraled down into the unconscious numerous times in my life, most notably in my mid-40s, when powerful, archetypal dreams started coming to me. I began to practice active imagination, going back into the dreams and letting them unfold in my conscious mind. These experiences often morphed into a kind of shamanic journey during which I met spirit guides who led me down into the earth and gave me visions of how to correct a situation or attitude. At times, I felt strong energy move through my body, aligning and grounding me in a very physical way. I would come back to regular consciousness after an hour or more, often shaken by the power of the experience, always feeling more connected to the roots of my being. When I had learned what I needed to know from these experiences, the dreams stopped. This is an example of connecting to the power of the Water phase.

Now is the time to turn your awareness to the unknown and the darkness within, trusting they have something important to teach you. The unconscious is the well from which you must drink if you are to fully experience the uniqueness of your life in all its richness. Ancient wisdom tells you to use your capacity for contemplation to face your fears and turn them into wisdom. You will not necessarily resolve all of your deep-seated issues; often that is just not possible, nor is it necessary. However, by shifting your awareness and coming into relationship with these issues, you garner self-knowledge and wisdom to use for your benefit as well as the healing of the world.

WILLPOWER

The Water phase asks us to look at our issues around willpower and our ability to manage the resources available to us. Willpower is the inner force that motivates us and gives us the strength to stay on the path we set in order to reach our goals. When in balance, we use willpower to cultivate our most important resources, self-knowledge and spiritual wisdom, to reach our potential in life.

My relationship with power has been ambivalent at best. I want it, yet I resist the responsibility that comes with it. I am attracted to power in others, yet also fear it might be used against me. I fear I will misuse power in the process of doing what it takes to get what I want. Like many, I have felt insecure at times, afraid I was neither using my power well nor living up to my potential.

Many of my patients report feeling fear and insecurity on a regular basis, as well as an inability to take action when needed. These are symptoms of imbalance in the Water phase. I hear their stories of dysfunction at work and in personal relationships, problems they avoid for long periods of time because it is just too difficult to face conflict. However, if we hope for peace of mind or to accomplish what we came here to do, a strategy of avoidance is not very effective. Instead, we can learn to use our willpower in skillful ways.

Engaging with life on a deeper level requires both self-awareness and an appropriate use of willpower. Two historical figures who exemplify the Water attributes of clear intelligence, unshakeable confidence in oneself and one's destiny, and extraordinary physical and mental endurance are Abraham Lincoln and Genghis Khan.

Abraham Lincoln worked tirelessly against tremendous opposition to obtain passage for the Thirteenth Amendment to the Constitution, which would abolish slavery in the United States. This was an immense achievement, something hardly anyone believed possible at the time. Lincoln was willing to patiently and deeply contemplate an issue and listen to the counsel of others, but always came back to his solitary reflections and self-knowledge. Lincoln engaged his willpower to accomplish what history asked of him and what he knew to be true, embracing responsibility for his unique destiny. What if he had given in to fears and become incapable of action? If he had not believed in himself and his own wisdom, the course of history would have been radically different.

Genghis Khan united the Mongol tribes, formed the largest empire ever known, and continued to rule until the time of his death in 1227. He was fearless and highly intelligent, displaying exceptional physical strength and endurance. He rode by horseback into unknown territory on campaigns lasting for years, into vast stretches of barren steppe and over treacherous mountain passes, never knowing what lay in store for him and his men. He embodied Water with an unwavering yet realistic belief in his strength, power, and own internal resources. Of course, he was also one of the most ruthless, cruel, and merciless men who ever lived, massacring millions and sparing only those few who could be useful to him.

While pursuing very different ends, these men bravely faced their fears and used all the resources at hand to achieve what many believed was impossible. Like all emotions, fear is part of the natural rhythms of life. However, allowing fear to stop us from developing our full potential is not necessary or natural at all. We all know on some level that if our unconscious fear makes us either too careful or too reckless, we will be unable to reach our goals.

Ancient wisdom shows us that when we reconnect authentically with our own wisdom and access our willpower, we can overcome the fears that may be paralyzing us. In the Water phase, return to the natural rhythm of listening deeply to what is happening within yourself and in the world. Engage with all your being in the felt experience of the present moment and thus place yourself in the flow of life. Reclaim your power as an individual and member of a global community, and contribute your unique wisdom to face the challenges presented to us at this time.

WATER IMBALANCE

- Depletes essence with excess work, exercise, sex, or alcohol
- Suffers weakness in low back, knees, or hearing
- Experiences infertility, poor childhood development, or premature aging
- Feels excessive fear and insecurity
- Lacks stamina, endurance, or motivation
- Symptoms worsen in winter or in cold climates

BALANCED WATER

- Wisely manages resources and deep reserves of energy
- Has strong knees, low back, hearing, and libido
- Displays good concentration and physical endurance
- Does not fear solitude, the inner world, or using power
- Cultivates a strong will and motivation to reach goals
- Is courageous, calm, and serene

CHALLENGE
STORAGE AND DORMANCY

The challenge of the Water phase is to surrender to a time of dormancy and stillness. Sit in silence and listen deeply to access the wisdom stored within the unconscious. Be emptied of all striving, die to your old ways of being, and allow the deep well of being to replenish you.

The Water phase, and the cold winter months it is associated with, is a time of dormancy, of waiting patiently and allowing a space for emptiness. We are not actively growing at this time, but rather must turn our attention to storing, or conserving, the energy of the body and assimilating the lessons of the Earth, Wood, Fire, and Metal phases. This is the time to slow down, withdraw a bit from the outer world, sit with and sleep on all we have taken in previously.

Water also represents the time of death—not just physical death, but the death of old ways of thinking and behaving. We may have a lot invested in the ideas, roles, and habits we have come to believe make up who we are. However, to access the potential for spiritual wisdom within ourselves, we must die many times to these old ways of being.

It may help if we think of death not as the opposite of life, but simply a part of the cycle of life. We see this in nature: In the depths of winter everything looks dead, but it is simply resting, waiting in silence and stillness for the right conditions for growth to return. Think of a seed, lying dormant in the cold, winter soil. It stores within itself the nutrients and potential necessary for life. It waits until the conditions are right to germinate and begin the cycle of renewal. Humans are meant to experience dormancy in a similar manner. If we take time to be spacious, silent, and still, we too can tap into the resources stored within as we embark upon new endeavors in life.

The Water phase demonstrates that life is not primarily about working to satisfy your desires and accumulate material wealth. Rather, the riches here are in self-knowledge. Cultivate spiritual wisdom by coming into relationship with all aspects of yourself, weaving together the lessons of the rhythms of change, and allowing the spaciousness of being. In the Water phase, you store both the energy of the physical body and the energy of the unconscious. To have the power to live your destiny, you must wisely use both the resources of the physical body and the capacity for consciousness you were given at birth.

> *One does not become enlightened by imagining figures of light, but by making the darkness conscious.*
> —Carl Jung

The unconscious mind is much more powerful than we might like to believe. It can be very constricting, withholding information from the conscious mind and disallowing access to the root and depths of our being. So often, what we hide away (even from ourselves) is our own unique light and wisdom. We must dive deeply into the unconscious and retrieve both our light and dark aspects in order to be fully integrated and gain access to the energy and potential buried within.

Years ago, a vivid dream showed me a truth about myself. In the dream, I am asked to go down into a basement storehouse to retrieve something. As I lay in wait in the dark basement, I see a young blond girl. She has come to get a jar of peaches, knows just where they are on a shelf in the corner, and takes them back up the now brightly lit stairs. This dream was much like a shamanic journey of soul retrieval. I am asked to go down into my unconscious (the dark basement storehouse), and there meet the part of myself (the young blond girl) who knows how to retrieve what is needed in the moment (the jar of peaches, a source of nourishment and sweetness), and take it back into the conscious world (the lit upstairs).

I later came to understand the deeper lesson of the dream: I had disowned the part of myself who has access to her inner knowing and is able to bring light and wisdom into daily life. I share this experience to emphasize the importance of paying close attention to your unconscious so you may connect to your own wisdom. We all have this knowing; we each must find our unique way to open to it.

Use dream work, meditation, shamanic journeying, or any techniques that work for you to relax the boundaries between your conscious and unconscious mind. Ancient wisdom understood this: Silence is essential if you are to be able to listen to your deepest self. For just a while, give yourself the gift of being quiet, stilling the incessant chattering of the mind, and simply listening. Listen without expectation, without the filters of conditioning, avoidance, fear, or of what you think of as "good" or "bad." You must befriend the wisdom available in the deeper realms to understand the root causes of your patterns of behavior, as well as to access other levels of consciousness.

THE INTERNAL ORGANS
KIDNEYS AND BLADDER

The kidneys regulate water metabolism and serve the body as a natural filter of the blood by removing waste that is excreted in the urine. These essential organs, each about the size of a fist, are located in the low back, at the level of the bottom of the rib cage. The bladder stores the urine produced by the kidneys until it is excreted.

The classic texts of Oriental medicine tell us the kidneys store the jing, a precious and limited essence that is meant to last our entire life. Closely related to the jing is what Oriental medicine calls *yuan qi,* the prenatal energy each of us receives from our parents and ancestors. Prenatal qi can be likened to the Western idea of the genetic code that determines our basic constitution. Both the jing and the prenatal qi are the resources, the deep reserves of energy, stored in the kidneys.

According to Oriental medicine, the kidneys play a vital role in endocrine and reproductive function. Chronic stress in the modern world overtaxes the kidney and may explain the rising incidence of low sperm counts and testosterone in men and hormonal imbalances in women. This is why practitioners of Oriental medicine treat the kidney in patients with infertility issues.

The kidneys also control hearing and give us the ability to listen attentively, not only physically, but also to our inner voice and to the voice of the world.

CINDY'S STORY
ADRENAL FATIGUE

Cindy came to the clinic with low back pain and dizziness upon standing. She said she felt tired and insecure most of the time. The onset of her symptoms was many months ago, just before her 50th birthday. After testing, her medical doctor had given her a diagnosis of adrenal fatigue.

When I asked her about the stresses in her life, Cindy told me that within a few years she had gone through a painful divorce and sold the family home, a close family member had died in a car accident, and she had moved and changed jobs several times. I commented that all of those events were major life transitions, so it was not surprising she was feeling the effects. She replied, "All my life I have been strong and healthy enough to do everything, and was able to push myself and make anything happen when applying my strong will. I am used to working hard and have a very active lifestyle. I often work all day and then spend hours in the evening making costumes and doing other jobs for local theater productions. I keep up with my friends, visiting and doing what I can to help them when they need it."

Cindy had not balanced the multiple stresses and chronic overwork in her life with rest, and now, years later, she was experiencing the depletion of the jing (or essence) of the Water phase. Cindy committed to following these basic guidelines for balancing Water:

- Eat well-cooked root vegetables, greens, and lean protein
- Drink a cup of warm water, broth, soup, or tea with each meal
- Do less and say no to nonessential demands on your time
- Schedule pauses in activity throughout the day in order to rest
- Avoid caffeine, alcohol, sugar, and highly stimulating environments
- Do restorative yoga, slow walks, qi gong, or other mild exercise daily

The jing is the deepest energy in the body, and it responds slowly to treatment. It took Cindy several years and much change to regain her health. She regularly saw a naturopath who helped her to regulate her nervous system, balance hormones, and rebuild the adrenals. The acupuncture and herbs she received at the clinic complemented the other healing modalities she used, but what helped her most was changing the way she lived and her daily habits.

"I know I will never have the energy and stamina I once had. I am also now aware that my system is much more sensitive than I ever wanted to admit. I went to trauma therapy recently and realized an early childhood trauma is behind the insecurity and fear I feel lately. The way I understand it now, I was guided from a deeply knowing place to this unconscious wound in order to heal it," she says.

Cindy is now back to work part-time, recently married, and moved into a new home. She has found the stability she needs to live simply by following the natural rhythms of the day without overdoing. In learning to balance the emotions of Water, she was able to transform her habitual insecurity to feelings of calm equanimity.

> We may not experience the effects of our excessive behaviors until years later, when we are much older. By then our essence has been depleted and there are no quick fixes. Be moderate in your habits now and conserve your energy to last a lifetime.

Adrenal Fatigue

The adrenals are glands that sit on top of the kidneys and release cortisol, a hormone that helps the body manage stress effectively. But cortisol is intended to help the body respond to emergencies, not the constant, multiple stresses of our demanding and overstimulating lives. With our bodies in a state of chronic stress, the natural rhythm of the adrenals gets out of balance and begins to secrete either too much or too little cortisol.

Our culture drives us to live in a way that depletes our essence and leaves us unfulfilled, tired, and old before our time. Even though we may live longer, many of us are not living better. As the researcher Brené Brown states, "We are the most in-debt, obese, addicted and medicated adult cohort in U.S. history." Sound familiar? It certainly does to me, as I have lived out this pattern myself and now see it on a weekly basis in the clinic.

We are encouraged to do everything to excess—work, exercise, eat, party, diet, consume, spend—and to frequently change jobs, homes, and partners, all in the name of seeking happiness. When we become exhausted from all this activity, some of us collapse on the couch or on a beach, hoping a brief rest will be enough to get us through the next day or year, until we can collapse again. Others misuse their willpower and force the body to carry on by using caffeine, sugar, chocolate, recreational and prescription drugs, alcohol, or sex— whatever helps them keep going.

Either way, we are numbing ourselves so we don't have to face our reality. When we decide to dull our fatigue and frustration, we cut ourselves off from the very wellspring of life. Instead, let us move toward balance in the Water phase by beginning to make choices to enhance our vitality and long-term health. (See Water Protocol for Adrenal Fatigue in part two for detailed information.)

WHERE ARE YOU IN THE WATER PHASE?

1. Am I aware of my attitudes about power, money, sex, and death?

2. Do I wisely use the resources of mind and body, not depleting them by excess?

3. Do I have balanced willpower, neither too cautious nor too reckless in pursuing my goals?

4. Do I have strong concentration and physical endurance?

5. Are my bones, hearing, low back, and knees strong?

6. Have I found ways to connect to my unconscious mind?

7. Do I hold some energy in reserve, never going to "empty"?

8. Do I make choices to simplify my life when possible?

9. Do I include periods of rest and unstructured time in my life?

10. Do I disconnect from devices and retreat in some way to regenerate?

If you can say yes more often than no (at least 80 percent of the time) to the above questions, congratulations! You embody many of the essential qualities of balance in this phase. If not, please contemplate what needs to happen to move you toward "yes" in this phase.

Everyone contains all five phases of change, in differing degrees, so stay open to seeing yourself in each phase.

THE ONE THING
REST

What I mean by rest here is unstructured downtime: time away from phones, schedules, appointment books, agendas, screens, and devices. We can make a choice to move through the day in a restful way, creating the spaciousness to respond to what calls to us in the moment, and listening to what deeper parts of us need. Rest may include the more traditional idea of a nap or sleep, but it can also be more dynamic.

When we rest in a way that includes unstructured downtime, we allow our vitality to be nourished and our potential for creativity to eventually bear fruit. Creative potential is like seeds resting underground, waiting for the right conditions to push up in the spring and grow up toward the light and warmth of the sun. The right conditions for birthing vitality and creativity include long, dark, insulated times of rest. If we learn the lessons of the Water phase, we will be able to move on successfully to the renewal of the Wood phase.

When we schedule every moment, we may be depleting the very source of energy needed to fuel us through an entire lifetime. So many families today are constantly booked with soccer practice, music and dance lessons, after-school enrichment programs, volunteer work, and evening tutoring or performances. Every day is filled to the max with worthwhile endeavors that they are committed to, whether or not they have the energy or desire to follow through.

As an adult, my family chose to allow space for rest in our lives. None of us overbooked ourselves with work, social, or educational demands. Instead, we made the conscious decision to value the quality of the present moment over striving too hard for something in the future. We left space in our daily routine so we could have the freedom to decide what natural rhythm we wanted to follow in the moment. Of course, there were some regularly scheduled activities, but for the most part we did our solid six to eight hours of work or school and were then free. If some big activity or great idea came up that we wanted to pursue, we had the reserves of energy to do so.

Why is it difficult for many of us to acknowledge our need to rest, even when we are ill or tired? In the clinic and with friends, I hear all the reasons that rest just is not possible, most having to do with lack of money or time. When I suggested taking a break to a friend working nonstop on a project, she glibly said, "I'll rest when I die." And there you have it. Many of us habitually act as though if we stopped and rested even for a short time, we might never get back up. You may want to believe that what you are doing is so important that you cannot stop. Perhaps it is easier to pretend that overdoing is not having an impact on your body or the people around you. Or you think you have no choice, you need the money, things will be different when...When, exactly?

If the idea of rest is foreign to you, start slowly. Set aside 30 minutes each day to decompress and truly rest, without the distraction of phone calls, texts, emails, the computer or TV, or anything else that takes you away from recharging. In the winter months, even if you do not live in a cold climate, it is important to follow the rhythm of the seasons and rest more. Remember: We need time to sit with what we have taken in from the other seasons and phases of Earth, Wood, Fire, and Metal. If we do not take this time to be spacious, silent, and still, we will not have rich reserves to tap into as we return to the renewal of spring and the Wood phase.

ADDRESSING RESISTANCE IN THE WATER PHASE

Those with an imbalance in the Water phase often have difficulty with focus, managing resources, and insecurity. Because of the choices we make, we do not have the time, money, or inner resources that would allow us to rest on a regular basis.

If you find yourself resisting the possibility of incorporating rest and unstructured downtime into your daily life, it may be time to look at the root beliefs or fears that are keeping you away from the benefits that await you. What is the real reason you are not allowing yourself this essential ingredient for long-term health? Is it because you believe that you do not deserve to rest? Are you afraid you will miss out on something or be judged as lazy? Perhaps if you stop, you will hear something you have been avoiding, something that needs attention or change? Or maybe you are addicted to stimulation and afraid of the spaciousness or emptiness of an unscheduled day?

Whatever the reason, it is okay. You are strong enough to face this within yourself now. It may be helpful to get support from a friend, coach, or mentor to look deeply at the ways you could, over time, make choices to change the way you live so there are fewer demands on your resources.

Many people are unable to take time off to rest as much as they need or would like to. They are working full time, or more, to pay bills, get kids through school, and help aging parents. If this is your life at the moment, please allow whatever time you can for yourself to rest. If this means an hour sitting quietly in the park on your day off or a nap while the kids are at a neighbor's house, great. Make a choice to take the time for yourself and rest. Let yourself enjoy that time to simply be, without filling those precious moments of spaciousness with more errands, work, or doing of any kind.

Most of us work much too hard and we make our practices all about ourselves eventually. We have even applied this work ethic to our spiritual lives. This is the danger of being too sincere, and of working too hard. At some point, we must understand it is no longer about us. That working too hard on ourselves is yet another way we have bought into the collective and that is of no real use....The seeker must make the transition from being focused on effort to being receptive to grace or she will remain in the sphere of the ego where there is no rebirth and no journey.

— **Llewellyn Vaughan-Lee**

RETREAT

Making time to withdraw from the stress and overwhelming demands of the world is a part of many cultures and most spiritual traditions. Sadly, in this country, retreat is perceived as a luxury for the few, not an essential part of life necessary to stay connected to the source of our vitality and well-being. As human beings, we need silence, stillness, and time to go inward and wait, to listen for what wants to come, to what needs attention in our body, in our life, and in the world.

Retreat takes many forms. Most emphasize silence, stillness, and quiet meditation or contemplation. Some retreats include reading sacred texts or chanting with music. Others incorporate service to others, such as simple cooking or cleaning chores for the retreat community.

The most important aspect of retreat is simplicity. We let go of outer demands and stimulation, the endless errands and expectations. We eat and live simply. We turn off our phones, disconnect from emails and social media, and allow for the empty space that is essential to reconnecting with ourselves. We retreat from the familiar, busy, outward-focused way in which we ordinarily live.

I am lucky to have a husband who was able and willing to take care of our son when he was younger and living at home, and partners at the clinic to care for my patients so I could take time off. Part of this is good fortune, but it is also the result of conscious choices I began making to simplify my life to allow time for retreat. It was important to me and I made it a priority. For the past 15 years, I have gone for week-long retreats during which I spend most of the time alone, in silence, walking, meditating, journaling, and reading. I claim this time for myself, and allow myself to do whatever I feel is needed in the moment, never imposing rigid rules on myself. This time is my gift to myself, a time to practice trusting the wisdom of my body and my inner knowing. The silence, meditation, and rest nourish me on deep levels, and I begin to feel whole again, and eventually, strong enough to return to the world and my responsibilities.

I am a very definite introvert and love being alone. However, most of the population, about 60 to 75 percent, is made up of extroverted personalities, people who are motivated and energized by being with others. For those of you who are extroverts, it may be more beneficial to start with a retreat that includes classes, teachings, and meals shared with others as well as times of solitude. There is a wide range of possibility to be explored within the concept of retreat. We do not have to spend much money or extended time away. We can begin by making a decision that, for a certain number of hours or days, we will not follow any social media. We will turn off our electronic devices and simply observe what happens within us with this simple yet profound choice.

If you find you like the freedom of being disconnected from media, you may want to try a brief retreat at home. You can simply post a "Do Not Disturb" sign and go to your room for a few precious hours of solitude to do whatever nourishes you: meditation, listening to music, reading inspirational texts, or journaling. There are also many retreat formats available on CD or online to do in the comfort of your own home, alone or with like-minded friends.

If you need more time to regenerate and look deeply within for what the next phase of life wants for you, try to arrange a longer-term retreat for yourself. If you have already fulfilled your responsibilities as a householder, parent, and participant in the workforce, a sabbatical can be the best gift you ever give yourself.

> *Let the waters settle and you will see the moon and the stars mirrored in your own being.*
> —**Rumi**

THE FOUR Rs OF WATER

The following suggestions are meant to help you internalize the lessons of the Water phase.

RECEIVE. Be open to finding a trusted therapist, coach, or guide to help you access the stored contents of your unconscious mind. You may be able to begin on your own, but most of us need the help of an experienced practitioner to delve deeply enough to get to the root causes and beliefs that govern us. Be open to the teachings offered by a spiritual teacher or community. Befriend your own unconscious mind, asking for dreams, images, and memories. Journal your insights. Collaborate with all your resources to unearth the root causes of your behavior and reconnect to your source.

REMEMBER. Tune in and listen, repeatedly, to the still, small voice of your inner self, as well as the teachings of the healers or spiritual traditions that resonate most with you. Insight alone is not enough for lasting change, so stay with the therapy or teachings until you get to the root causes and see your behaviors changing. Never push yourself too hard or get so tired you feel you are on empty, with no reserves. It is difficult to build up from zero, so always hold some of your energy back for yourself.

REFLECT. Fear and insecurity may have protected you from situations that would have been harmful to you in the past. Reflect on your current circumstances and relationships. Is the way you are living in harmony with the essence of who you are in the present? If not, listen inwardly to what is needed to engage your self-knowledge and willpower to achieve your goals.

RETURN. Return to yourself, your body, and the Earth phase during transitions from one season or phase to the next. Take whatever time you need to digest and assimilate what you have learned here and make it your own. This is the way to lasting transformation.

PART TWO

COMMON SENSE SUGGESTIONS AND
PROTOCOLS FOR THE FIVE PHASES

FINDING BALANCE

The choices we make each day move us either toward or away from balance in our lives. Often we want to add more to our lives before we have made space for it by letting something else go. We all know what that feels like: We get overwhelmed by trying to do too much and eventually return to our old patterns, convinced that change is impossible. I would like to offer you a different perspective that has proven successful for me and my patients.

This part of *Rhythms of Change* presents simple protocols designed to help you make informed choices in each of the five phases of change. You will be reminded of actions that lead toward balance in each phase, followed by questions to spark your curiosity about how the material relates to you. For each phase, I offer nutritional guidelines for you to explore and observe how your body responds. My hope is that you will gradually experience more freedom and ease with nutritional choices. Explore and learn to eat intuitively, including foods, tastes, and textures that provide your body with authentic nourishment and satisfaction.

Also included in this section are phase-specific protocols to address the imbalances discussed earlier in part one. These suggestions are meant to offer you an effective beginning to your journey toward better health. It is generally a good idea to consult with a practitioner to customize these suggestions to your specific needs, especially if you are dealing with serious or chronic health issues. My written suggestions are not meant to serve as personal medical advice or as a substitute for the attention of a practitioner. Please listen to your own body and gather information to make the choices that are right for you. See Recommended Resources in the appendices for information on finding qualified health care practitioners.

For best results, follow the guidelines given here quite closely at first, until you feel much better. This will afford you a *felt* experience that brings home the fact that what you consume makes a difference in how you feel. After that, you can follow what is known as the 80/20 rule: Follow the plan 80 percent of the time and give yourself more freedom the other 20 percent. This approach requires that you choose to eat what really nourishes your body four out of five times, but still allows you space to indulge without unwanted side effects.

Change is not always easy, and rarely does it happen as quickly as we would like. However, if we look to the wisdom of the rhythms of change inherent in nature and within each of us, change is possible. As you follow the common sense guidelines set out in this part of the book, remember to also reflect on the ancient wisdom of each of the five phases: Earth teaches you to be centered in your body, receive the nourishment available to you, and make mature choices to transform your habits and your life. Wood helps you get out of the way of life, cultivate the strong energy of self assertion to gain perspective on your purpose, and allow something new to be born within you. Fire teaches you to use the oneness of heart and mind to fully express yourself, to live, love, and use balanced control to do what is necessary to reach your goals. Metal asks you to open to inspiration, harvest what is valuable to you and let go of what is not, and gives you the strength to focus inwardly on spirit. Finally, Water shows you how to dive deeply to harness the dormant power of the unconscious, to cultivate balanced willpower and self-knowledge, and to die to your old ways of being.

Please be patient and gentle with yourself, slowly and gradually incorporating the ideas, practices, and behaviors presented in this book. Befriend and get into relationship with the many aspects of yourself that are described here. Live your life as fully and as authentically as you can, including everything—yes, even the days of being weary, unmotivated, or disheartened, please—and one day you will wake up to find you are a new person and have participated in the miracle of changing your mental and physical habits into ones that are life enhancing for you and your loved ones. I trust you can do this. Believe that you can!

MOVING TOWARD BALANCE
IN THE EARTH PHASE

Reminder: The challenge of the Earth phase is to make mature choices to balance all forms of consumption and transform your behaviors to live with rhythmic moderation. You must learn to identify and satisfy your authentic needs for nourishment and accept reasonable limitations.

ACTIONS

Begin transitioning to a whole foods diet by eating one or more of your favorite whole foods each day.

Make mature choices to balance all forms of consumption, including mental stimulation, with moderate physical exercise and rest.

Each day look for, and name, one thing you are grateful for in your life.

GET CURIOUS ABOUT YOURSELF

What form of nourishment do you need at this time? Remember, food is only one of many ways to get your authentic needs met.

What gives you a feeling of satisfaction? What can you do to experience being enough or having enough more often?

What are you willing to do this week to incorporate the above actions into your daily life?

EATING TO BALANCE EARTH

Earth phase foods are fresh, mild, and simply prepared, with few ingredients. Earth phase foods are appropriate in every season, but the transformative and centering qualities of Earth are especially needed during transitions between seasons and at times of cold weather, low energy, or illness. Think of Earth as home base: If you slip up occasionally, no worries. Just come back to home base and eat within the scope of Earth to get back on track. Follow these eating guidelines to balance Earth:

- Eat mainly cooked, warm foods.

- Eat moderately and at regular intervals, never skipping meals.

- Soup, stew, broth, and congee are cooked well, and thus easy to digest.

- Drink a cup of hot water or tea with meals, especially if the meal itself is not cooked and warm.

- Chew well and eat slowly. Enzymes for digestion are secreted in the mouth, so take your time to enhance the assimilation of what you eat.

- Yellow-to-orange-colored foods or foods with a mild, sweet flavor benefit Earth. Examples are carrot, apple, summer squash, brown rice, and sweet potato. Congee, a well-cooked grain porridge, is a perfect food for the Earth phase. (See appendices for a congee recipe.)

The Pancreas, Blood Sugar Regulation, and a Whole Foods Diet

The yin organ of the Earth phase is the pancreas (or spleen–pancreas, as it is known in Oriental medicine). The pancreas is interesting because it is both an endocrine gland, producing the hormones insulin and glucagon to regulate blood sugar levels, and an exocrine gland that secretes digestive enzymes to break down the food we consume.

Sugar was once a delicacy, something our ancestors ate only on rare occasions. Now almost every processed food contains sugar, and we love to eat bread, pasta, rice, and potatoes. These are high-glycemic foods that are quickly converted to simple sugars in the bloodstream. This causes a rise in blood sugar and a subsequent spike in insulin release. Over time, repeated consumption of these foods weakens the digestive function and may lead to diabetes and obesity.

It is important to transition to a whole foods diet that includes proteins, vegetables, and healthy fats. This foundation of sound nutrition to balance blood sugar, combined with a more moderate approach to consumption of sugar and refined carbohydrates, is an effective way to improve your overall health.

ONE WEEK PROTOCOL FOR BLOOD SUGAR IMBALANCE

Balancing your blood sugar is one of the most important things you can do to improve your health and a key component of managing imbalances in every phase. During the first couple of days without refined carbohydrates, you may feel fatigue, headaches, or other uncomfortable symptoms as your body cleanses itself after years of overconsumption. But if you stick to the simple guidelines given here, you will soon feel better than ever.

Symptoms of blood sugar imbalance

- Fatigue
- Sleepiness after meals
- Cravings for sugar and other carbs
- Mental fogginess
- Energy and mood fluctuations during the day
- Abdominal weight gain or difficulty losing weight
- Irritability between meals
- Insomnia or waking at night

The most important things to keep in mind when working to balance blood sugar are reducing your carbohydrate consumption and eating frequently. Do not let yourself go hungry; in fact, you may need to eat even if you do not feel hungry.

Get a pocket carbohydrate counter or find an online carb counter, such as www.calorieking.com, to use as a reference tool. The only thing you are counting at this point is total carbohydrates. Do not worry about fats or calories during this one-week protocol.

The initial stage of this protocol requires one week of closely following the guidelines set out below. Most people begin to feel the benefits in that short time and want to continue eating this way, in a modified form, for the rest of their lives.

Most people need to reduce their carbohydrate consumption to 60 to 80 grams daily to beat the carb addiction. Keep the total number of carbohydrates you consume to 60 to 80 grams a day for the first week. It may sound difficult now, but I know you can do this for one week!

EATING GUIDELINES

This one-week protocol allows for an abundance of tasty and satisfying foods, so you can adapt it to suit your own taste and lifestyle. It is also meant to be easy and not time-consuming.

- Eat a diet of whole, unprocessed, low-glycemic foods consisting of protein, vegetables, and healthy fats. (See the list below for ideas.)
- Include protein and fat every time you eat. Fat will control your hunger, make you feel full, and satisfy essential nutrient needs to help eliminate cravings.
- Never skip meals, especially breakfast. This will keep your blood sugar, brain chemistry, energy, and mood stable.
- Eat every three hours. Even if you do not feel hungry, eat something. You may not feel the effects when your blood sugar

drops, and thus cannot use your perception of hunger as a signal to eat. You do not have to eat a full meal; a snack that includes protein and fat is fine.

- Eat five to 10 servings of fresh vegetables daily (except those that are high-glycemic). This is essential in order to provide the nutrients and fiber the body needs as well as to balance the protein and fat.

- Exercise is vital for increasing energy, reducing insulin resistance, and improving blood-glucose metabolism. If you do not already exercise, start moving!

- If you eat dairy products, they must be full fat to balance the milk sugar (lactose) they contain.

- Drink approximately eight glasses (64 ounces) of water per day. Often we think we are hungry when actually the body simply needs to be hydrated. Green tea and sparkling water with lime are also good choices.

- If you are in a rush, use protein drinks, made with rice, pea, or whey protein (not soy), rather than skip a meal or have a nutritionally inadequate meal.

- Do not drink caffeine on an empty stomach.

- Avoid alcohol, which is high in sugar.

- Avoid artificial sweeteners. Your body recognizes the sweet taste and will release insulin in response, as it thinks carbohydrates are on the way.

- Eliminate breads, potatoes, soy, grains, fruit, and sugar in all forms.

- Eliminate sodas, fruit juice, carrot juice, and smoothies.

Low-Glycemic Food Choices

Proteins: Meat, fish, eggs, beans, lentils, seeds, nuts (including nut butters), whole-fat dairy.

Fresh vegetables: All your favorite non-starchy veggies, while avoiding the starchy vegetables like white potatoes, root vegetables, and winter squash.

Healthy fats: Butter, ghee, cold- or expeller-pressed unrefined olive oil, coconut oil, and un-sweetened coconut milk, as well as the healthy fats in avocados and the proteins listed above.

If you feel you cannot eliminate all grains and fruit during this one-week protocol, include one-third cup cooked brown rice, quinoa, millet, or regular oatmeal and one-half cup unsweetened berries per day.

Focus on foods that satisfy your authentic nutritional needs. The body responds well to being nourished.

Eat a combination of protein, fat, and veggies at every meal and snack.

Never, ever, skip breakfast. Eating a breakfast containing protein and good-quality fat is essential to stabilize your blood sugar, energy, and mood.

Do not go hungry. Eat every three hours, consuming as much of the allowed foods as you need to feel satisfied.

Suggestions to Keep it Simple

To help you adjust to a new way of eating, try some of the following meal ideas.

Breakfast

- Eggs with your favorite veggies and avocado, or with ham and cheese
- Breakfast salad with greens, tomato, cheese, seeds, and hard-boiled eggs
- Plain Greek yogurt (one-half cup serving)
- Quick morning porridge: Add 1 cup boiling water to 2 tablespoons each of hemp seed, chia seed, and unsweetened coconut milk. Stir well and add blueberries. Let sit for five minutes before eating. Adjust amount of water to get desired consistency.
- Nut butter or cheese with celery
- Dinner for breakfast: Eat last night's leftover lentil soup or salmon and veggies.
- Whey protein shake with ground flax, hemp, chia, or almonds, blueberries, one-third cup unsweetened coconut milk or 1 tablespoon coconut oil

Lunch and Dinner

Have a baked or grilled protein and two large servings of vegetables, veggie soup, or salad. Add butter to cooked foods and olive oil to salads, and cook with coconut oil or ghee for essential healthy fats.

- Mixed veggie salad with hummus, avocado, and nuts
- Chicken, egg, or tuna salad on a bed of greens
- Lentil and veggie soup
- Quiche or veggie omelet with salad or soup
- Grilled chicken or salmon with steamed, mixed vegetables

- Chicken and vegetable soup, with one third cup brown rice added if desired

- Fried eggs on a bed of black beans, topped with salsa and avocado

- Baked chicken with roasted carrots, onions, and turnips; sautéed broccoli

Snack Tips

Always have snacks and water with you, in the car and at work.

Make a note or set an alarm to remind you to eat every three hours.

Good snacks include mixed nuts, nut butter packets, hummus, cheese, beef or turkey jerky, hard-boiled eggs, smoked salmon, lunchmeat rollups, sliced avocado, celery, red or yellow peppers, cucumbers, baby carrots, cherry tomatoes.

Coconut oil in a cup of hot tea will satisfy your hunger and not spike your blood sugar.

Do not rely on protein or energy bars. Most are so concentrated they tax your digestion; they may also be high in carbohydrates. Use them only in a pinch, as this is a processed product, not a whole food.

AFTER THE ONE-WEEK PROTOCOL

What comes after the one-week protocol is up to you! You may decide to continue on the same protocol for several more weeks, or modify it to include slightly more carbohydrates. When you feel your body is ready, slowly reintroduce more carbs into your diet. Have a small portion (one-third cup, cooked) of brown rice, millet, or quinoa (instead of pasta, white rice or white potatoes). Or include some sweet potatoes and winter squash in your diet. Watch how you feel. Better or not? If you are sleepy after meals or craving sugar, you have had too many carbohydrates and will want to reduce consumption of high-carb foods until you are again symptom free.

When your blood sugar is consistently stable, maintain your carbohydrate consumption at 100 to 150 grams daily, if you can do so without experiencing any of the symptoms listed at the beginning of this protocol. Resume your exploration of intuitive eating to satisfy your authentic nutritional needs for long-term health. And know you can return to this protocol for balancing blood sugar whenever your body needs it.

I have not included optional supplements in this chapter as I sincerely believe this saying by Hippocrates, "Let food be thy medicine and medicine be thy food." Please read the Nutrition Basics for All Phases chapter in part two for more information. Consider getting acupuncture and an herbal formula from a nationally certified acupuncturist to balance Earth and help correct any blood sugar imbalance.

MOVING TOWARD BALANCE
IN THE WOOD PHASE

Reminder: The challenge of the Wood phase is to be attentive and let go of any mental rigidity in order to clearly see what is ready to be born within you and in the world. Open yourself to what wants to come next, and take action to renew yourself and your purpose in life.

ACTIONS

Begin incorporating some form of exercise into your life, building up to 30 minutes most days.

Be alert to insights you receive as to what wants to come next; make plans and take action on one of them.

Practice kindness and forgiveness for yourself for any mistakes you may have made.

GET CURIOUS ABOUT YOURSELF

What wants to be born or renewed in your life? How are you willing to assert yourself to make it a reality?

What helps you feel authentic kindness toward yourself and others? What can you do to experience this feeling more often?

What are you willing to do this week to incorporate one of the above actions into your daily life?

EATING TO BALANCE WOOD

The Wood phase corresponds with the season of spring, a time of expansion, birth, and renewal. Follow these eating guidelines to balance Wood:

- Add more fruits and vegetables into your daily diet, especially greens.

- Add some raw and sprouted foods to your meals, if digestion is not weak.

- Eat less and more lightly at this time to cleanse the body after the heavier, warming diet of winter.

- Prepare foods simply. The ideal is a short cooking time at a high temperature, like stir-frying or sautéing.

- Green-color foods and sour-flavor foods benefit Wood. Examples are fresh greens, asparagus, sprouts, celery, peas, artichoke, parsley, lemon, lime, grapefruit, and sour plum (umeboshi).

- Avoid fatty meats, fried foods, coffee, sugar, alcohol, drugs, preservatives, and food additives.

FUNCTIONS OF THE LIVER

The liver, the yin organ of the Wood phase, has multiple and complex functions. It produces bile, which breaks down fats and prepares them for assimilation in the intestinal tract. It also stores glycogen, which plays an important role in blood-sugar regulation. An organ of detoxification, the liver clears impurities from the body and regulates a wide variety of other biochemical reactions, including hormone metabolism.

Wood imbalances may arise when we ingest substances that are toxic or build up an excess over time. The liver is also responsible for hormonal balance and must be addressed whenever we experience symptoms of PMS, peri-menopause, menopause, or low adrenal function.

PROTOCOL FOR HORMONAL BALANCE

When we are in balance, our hormones follow a natural rhythm of daily, monthly, and lifelong cycles. Following are discussions of important lifestyle factors that can disrupt that rhythm, along with guidelines to help bring you back into harmony with yourself.

Symptoms of hormonal imbalance

- Digestive troubles, especially fat digestion
- Mood swings
- Irritability and agitation
- Depression and anxiety
- Feeling easily frustrated or overwhelmed
- Hot flashes or night sweats
- Insomnia
- Bloating and edema
- Menstrual cramps
- Inability to relax, feeling "tired and wired"

BASIC GUIDELINES FOR BALANCING HORMONES

The liver has an influential role in digestion and detoxification, so many of the following are diet-related suggestions.

- Eat fresh. Add a lot more fresh veggies and a bit more fruit to your daily diet. Eat some of these fresh veggies raw, and steam or stir-fry others.
- Think green. Green veggies are filled with magnesium and chlorophyll that alkalinize the blood, relax the muscles, calm the mind, and restore the liver. Eat veggies lightly steamed; or blend into a smoothie and drink first thing in the morning for optimal liver-cleansing effect. High quality chlorella tablets are also very good for the liver.

- First thing each morning, drink a small glass of room-temperature water with the fresh juice of half a lemon, lime, or grapefruit. Or find a good herbal digestive bitters formula and take it before each meal. This will stimulate movement in the liver.

- Add foods rich in magnesium and calcium to calm the nervous system and nourish the body. For magnesium, choose dark, leafy greens (such as chard, kale, or raw spinach), flax and pumpkin seeds, tahini (sesame butter), lentils, brown rice, avocado, banana, and dried figs. For calcium, add full-fat milk or Greek yogurt, tahini, cooked greens, red kidney beans, canned sardines, and curly kale.

- Be sure to get enough fiber. Fiber binds with fat, cholesterol, excess hormones, and toxins in your intestines and speeds them through the digestive tract. The average American consumes only 15 grams of fiber a day, but two or three times that amount is actually needed for optimal health. Aim for 30 to 50 grams of fiber daily. If your diet doesn't provide enough to keep your bowels moving daily, freshly grind 2 tablespoons of flax seed (in a coffee grinder) and mix in water. Take first thing in the morning. (See Metal: Protocol for Constipation for more information.)

- Consume less. Make a choice to reduce the quantity of food, drinks, snacks, and supplements you consume, especially rich and fatty foods. Take out all the foods that damage or slow liver function (as noted above). Some people may want to eat a restricted diet of mainly cooked and raw veggies, with some fresh fruit, for several days. Others can simply eliminate all harmful substances while slowly adding healthier recommendations.

- Stay hydrated, drinking eight glasses of water daily. Substitute green tea for coffee.

- Balancing blood sugar and managing stress are essential for balanced liver and hormonal function. Please see Protocol for Balancing Blood Sugar and the Stress and Health chapter for more information.

- Consider getting acupuncture and an herbal formula from a nationally certified acupuncturist to balance Wood and help correct your hormonal issues.

HORMONAL BALANCE, EXERCISE, AND MOOD

Exercise helps immensely to optimize the many functions of the liver, including the regulation of hormonal balance and the harmonious flow of our emotional energy. Exercise regularly, in the outdoors with natural light if possible. Whatever you decide to do, just be sure to move daily. Begin slowly if you don't already exercise, and build up to at least 30 minutes daily.

The classic texts tell us the liver is the organ of temperament and emotion. It is no wonder, considering the all-encompassing tasks it must perform, that the liver has a tendency to become congested due to dietary imbalance or emotional repression. Emotion is just another form of energy, and it too needs to move. When the liver qi circulates freely and easily, the energy of the entire body moves, optimizing vitality and mood at the same time.

For Chronic Hormonal Imbalance

Add nutrient-dense and green foods from this protocol to your daily diet and exercise vigorously at least four times per week. Absolutely avoid sugar and simple carbohydrates in all forms: grains, breads, potatoes, soy, and most fruits. Avoid fatty meats, fried foods, alcohol, caffeine, chocolate, and recreational drugs to lessen the load on your liver. Consult your practitioner for an herbal formula and take it consistently until your symptoms lessen.

OPTIONAL SUPPLEMENTS

You may need additional calcium, magnesium, and B vitamins, especially B6, in your diet to address the effects of stress and hormonal imbalance. Almost 75 percent of us are deficient in magnesium because we do not eat a nutrient-rich diet. Magnesium deficiency can exacerbate all the symptoms of hormonal imbalance, including fatigue, insomnia, irritability, and anxiety.

The following is a list of nutritional supplements that may be used for hormonal imbalance. Talk to your practitioner to see if any of them are appropriate for you, or consult with a qualified herbalist to get a customized herbal formula.

Nutritional supplements

Take 1000 mg combined of DHA/EPA one to two times daily. See Appendices for more information on what to look for in Omega-3 fatty acid supplements

Magnesium chelate:† 300 to 600 mg at bedtime. Begin with 300 mg nightly, adding an additional 300 mg if needed

Calcium chelate:† 500 mg/day

Vitamin B-50 complex:‡ 2 tablets a day

---

†I recommend Albion chelated minerals for optimal absorption such as those from Designs for Health.

‡Spray or sublingual vitamin B complex is a good option, as it is easily absorbed.

MOVING TOWARD BALANCE
IN THE FIRE PHASE

Reminder: The challenge of the Fire phase is to embrace your dreams, tap into your passion, and unite the wisdom of heart and mind to fully live your life. You must wholeheartedly want to grow, develop your consciousness, and work diligently to manifest the truth of who you are in the world, without overdoing.

ACTIONS

Begin including restful sleep, giving yourself at least seven to eight hours of uninterrupted sleep most nights.

Identify one dream you are willing to work to manifest in your life, and take the first step towards it.

Restore your sense of play by doing something enlivening or that makes you laugh.

GET CURIOUS ABOUT YOURSELF

What goals can you name for yourself at this time? What are you willing to do to exert the control and self-discipline necessary to achieve them?

What gives you a feeling of joy or connection? What can you do to experience this more often?

What are you willing to do this week to incorporate one of the above actions into your daily life?

EATING TO BALANCE FIRE

The Fire phase corresponds with the season of summer. It is the time of upward movement, warmth, growth, and manifestation. Follow these eating guidelines to balance Fire:

- Eat less and lightly during the hot months, including many fresh vegetables and fruits. However, be careful not to consume cold or raw foods in excess. These foods may weaken digestion.

- Hydrate adequately. Since we are sweating more in the heat, we need to eat moisture-filled foods, such as cucumber and watermelon, and drink plenty of water. Remember that sweating is the body's way of cooling off, and hot liquids can help induce sweating.

- Prepare simple meals containing only a few fresh ingredients.

- Cook foods very lightly by quickly steaming or simmering for a minute or two. If sautéing, use high heat for only a short time.

- Choose red-colored and bitter-flavored foods to benefit Fire. Examples are red bell pepper, tomato, romaine lettuce, beet, chiles, watermelon, persimmon, raspberries, and bitter melon.

THE HEART AND RESTFUL SLEEP

The heart is the yin organ of the Fire phase and is considered the ruler of all the organs. The classic texts of Oriental medicine say the heart houses the mind, meaning the heart is the center of emotional and mental activity. It is in charge of consciousness, thinking, sleep, and *shen,* which translates as "spirit." The energy of the heart needs to be calm and settled in order for sleep to be possible. When the heart is out of balance, insomnia may result. Losing even an hour or two of sleep a night over time can lead to major health issues.

Good-quality sleep is essential for long-term health, strong immune response, weight management, and all cognitive function. If you are not getting enough sleep, your body and mind are not getting the time they need to rest and regenerate. The body needs to follow a natural rhythm of waking and sleeping to function optimally.

PROTOCOL FOR INSOMNIA

By insomnia, I mean disruption of any kind that prevents you from getting adequate and quality sleep on a regular basis. This includes inability to fall asleep or to stay asleep, waking more than once in the night, or inability to fall back asleep after waking in the night.

Most adults need at least seven or eight hours of uninterrupted sleep; adolescents need at least nine to ten hours. Sleep is not separate from the other activities of daily life. Many lifestyle factors can influence the quality of your sleep, from what you eat to how much exercise you get and the level of stress you are experiencing. It is essential you pay attention to the choices you make each day so the mind, body, and spirit will be calm at bedtime and allow you to fall into a deep and restful sleep.

Factors that contribute to insomnia

- Light at night, particularly from electronic devices
- Staying up too late (past 11:00 p.m.)
- Eating late at night
- Blood sugar imbalance
- Caffeine, alcohol, and recreational drugs
- Overstimulation of any kind, including excessive noise, emotions, or light
- Chronic stress that makes you unable to relax
- Hormonal imbalance causing hot flashes or night sweats
- Lack of exercise
- Lack of essential nutrients or amino acids to balance and calm the nervous system

Develop a rhythmic schedule for sleep, along with a regular schedule of meals and exercise. Try to wake up and go to sleep at about the same time every day, with only occasional exceptions, allowing for at least seven to nine hours of uninterrupted sleep.

BASIC GUIDELINES FOR RESTFUL SLEEP

- Turn off all devices one to two hours before bed. Bright screens are very stimulating to the mind and may disrupt melatonin, the sleep hormone.

- Cover bedroom windows with dark shades or wear a sleep mask if there is too much light in the bedroom.

- Go to bed by 10:00 or 11:00 pm. Research shows that sleep is more regenerative in the hours before midnight.

- Eat your last meal of the day by 7:00 p.m., or two to three hours before sleep, so digestion is complete before bedtime.

- Avoid caffeine and alcohol as both disrupt sleep. If you consume caffeine, do not have any after 12:00 p.m. This includes chocolate as well as coffee, tea, soda, and chai.

- Use earplugs and a white noise machine if there is too much external noise.

- Expose yourself to natural light. Going outside during the day will help your body regulate the sleep hormone melatonin, which requires daylight for optimal function.

- Use a light therapy* device mid-October through mid-March to help regulate sleep and mood during the winter months, especially if you live north of Florida. The sun is not strong enough in northern locations in the winter for us to get the natural light we need. Light therapy is particularly valuable if you have chronic (not occasional) insomnia.

- Exercise daily to satisfy the body's need for physical activity. For best results, don't exercise after dinner or too close to bedtime.

- Unstable blood sugar will trigger a hormonal chain reaction that can disrupt sleep, either by making it difficult to fall asleep or waking you up in the night. Blood sugar levels need to be stable all day, most days, to improve the quality of sleep. Eat adequate protein and healthy fat at dinnertime. Before bed have a snack of a large teaspoon of almond or sesame butter (tahini), or drink a cup of herbal tea with a teaspoon of coconut oil or a glass of warm milk (full fat, please).

- Add foods rich in magnesium and calcium to your daily diet to calm the nervous system. These nutrients are essential for deep sleep. Good sources of magnesium are dark, leafy greens (such as chard, kale, or raw spinach), flax and pumpkin seeds, tahini (sesame butter), lentils, brown rice, avocado, banana, and dried figs. For calcium, include full-fat milk or Greek yogurt, tahini, cooked greens, red kidney beans, canned sardines, and curly kale.

- Take a soothing bath before bed: Put 2 cups Epsom salts, a half-cup baking soda, and 10 drops lavender essential oil in a hot bath and soak for 20 minutes or more.

- Consider getting acupuncture and an herbal formula from a nationally certified acupuncturist to balance Fire and help correct your sleep problems.

- To learn about amino acid therapy that may help with chronic insomnia, read *The UltraMind Solution* by Mark Hyman, MD.

---

*I have found the Philips goLITE BLU Light Therapy Device to be very effective. I use it myself every winter.

Relaxation Tip

If you are having trouble falling asleep or you wake in the night, try to calm your mind by focusing on your breath. With each breath, relax a part of your body, letting go of any tension. Start with your head and work your way down to your feet. Slowly bring your energy down from the head and upper chest, away from the constant pull of thoughts and emotions, down to the abdomen into the center of your being, and finally, into the legs and feet. If you are still awake, bring your awareness into the abdomen below the umbilicus and continue to focus your breathing there. When your mind gets distracted with worries or thoughts, come back to the breath in the lower abdomen and rest there.

OPTIONAL SUPPLEMENTS

To improve sleep quickly while you incorporate the above suggestions, supplements can be helpful. Speak with your practitioner or refer to *The UltraMind Solution* for additional suggestions.

Nutritional supplements

Consider taking one or two of these supplements in the evening, 30 minutes before bed:

Sleep & Relax or *Sound Sleep* by Gaia Herbs. Dosage as per label instructions

Magnesium chelate:* 300 to 600 mg nightly. Begin with 300 mg nightly, adding another dose if needed

Calcium chelate:* 500 mg nightly

L-theanine:† 200 mg nightly

5-HTP (5-hydroxytryptophan):‡ 100 mg, 1 or 2 capsules nightly

---

*I recommend Albion chelated minerals for optimal absorption such as those from Designs for Health.

†Look for products containing Suntheanine, a proprietary L-theanine extract.

‡Choose a product that includes 20 mg of Vitamin B6 per 100 mg of 5-HTP to optimize absorption.

MOVING TOWARD BALANCE
IN THE METAL PHASE

Reminder: The challenge of the Metal phase is to open yourself to inspiration and harvest what is valuable in your life. Let go of what no longer furthers your growth and develop the strength to grieve important losses. Set your focus on wholeness, looking beyond superficial appearances to connect more deeply to life and spirit.

ACTIONS

Engage the power of mindful breathing by including at least 10 to 15 minutes of this practice most days.

Reflect on how you would like to add value to another or to the world. Take the first step.

Explore your thoughts, feelings, and inner world through careful observation and journaling to reconnect to yourself.

GET CURIOUS ABOUT YOURSELF

What do you value and want to become more committed to in your life? What do you need to let go of in order for this to be possible?

What inspires you or awakens a deep longing within you? How can you experience this more often?

What are you willing to do this week to incorporate one of the above actions into your daily life?

EATING TO BALANCE METAL

The Metal phase corresponds with the season of autumn, a time of contraction, harvest, and decline. Follow these eating guidelines to balance Metal:

- Cook foods longer, at lower temperatures; appropriate methods include baking and sautéing. Longer cooking fulfills the body's needs at this time by making foods more concentrated and heartier.

- Eat slowly and chew well to facilitate digestion, as in all phases.

- Excess dryness harms Metal, so include foods that moisten the respiratory tract and intestines: unsweetened coconut milk, olive and coconut oils, avocado, sesame seed, spinach, seaweeds, honey, milk, butter, dark-green leafy veggies, and congee.

- Choose white-color foods and pungent, spicy flavors to benefit Metal. Examples are turnip, leek, cabbage, parsnips, cauliflower, potato, sauerkraut, onion, garlic, ginger, and pear.

THE LUNGS, IMMUNITY, AND MINDFUL BREATHING

The lungs are the yin organ of the Metal phase. In the classic texts, the lungs are said to be in charge of the protective energy, or *wei qi*. The lungs must be very strong indeed to fight off dryness, heat, cold, wind, and damp, as well as the bacteria and viruses in our environment. Frequent colds, flus, and other illnesses are a sign of a weak Metal phase and decreased immune function.

Mindful breathing strengthens the lungs, increases energy, reduces stress, and thus improves the immune system. The breath is our connection between mind and body. Being aware of the breath brings us to the present moment, the only one that holds any potential for change and healing. Mindful breathing is a fundamental practice for a balanced Metal phase.

PROTOCOL FOR IMPROVED IMMUNE SYSTEM FUNCTION

As with most programs, start by adding positive behaviors and nutrient-dense foods before you eliminate life-depleting foods and behaviors. We are able to maintain a program that nourishes and satisfies our authentic needs much easier than one that leaves us feeling deprived.

- Eat nourishing, whole foods, mostly cooked and warm.

- Get enough rest, sleeping seven to nine hours every night. (See Fire Protocol for Insomnia for detailed suggestions.)

- Stay well hydrated, drinking half your body weight in ounces of water daily.

- Reduce stress in whatever ways work for you. (See Stress and Health chapter for suggestions.)

- Use a neti pot or other form of sinus irrigation daily to remove pollens, mucus, and unhealthy bacteria from the nose and sinus cavities. This practice is good for prevention and essential during a cold or sinus infection.

- Eat two cloves of fresh garlic daily, or take in enteric-coated pill form.

- Use a cool air humidifier in your home, especially in the bedroom, to counteract the dryness of the autumn and winter seasons. Mucous membranes function better when moist.

- Wash hands frequently when exposed to public environments or those who are ill.

- Optimize your vitamin D levels. Have your vitamin D3 level checked by a simple blood test. Ideally, it should be within the therapeutic range of 60 to 80 ng/ml.

- Exercise increases the vital qi of the lungs and strengthens the immune system. Therefore, it is of utmost importance to exercise the lungs through adequate physical activity. Aim for at least 30 minutes of vigorous movement daily.

- Consider getting acupuncture and an herbal formula from a nationally certified acupuncturist to balance Metal and help correct your immune system problems.

OPTIONAL SUPPLEMENTS

The supplements listed below can be extremely helpful to enhance immune function. See Home Treatment for the Common Cold in the appendices for effective herbal formulas, including strong antiviral and antibacterial herbs, for treating colds and flu.

Nutritional supplements

Emulsified vitamin D3, if levels are low: 2,000 IU/day

Mushroom Kings by Bio Essence: 3 capsules daily

Echinacea Goldenseal by Gaia Herbs. As per dosage instructions on the label

---

THE LARGE INTESTINE AND CONSTIPATION

The large intestine takes mostly digested material from the small intestine and absorbs excess water from it, and eliminates the stool. If the large intestine fails to properly do its job, the result will be either constipation or loose stools.

Constipation means you have a complete bowel movement less than once per day, you are straining to eliminate, or you pass small pellets instead of large, fully formed stools. It is essential to keep the bowels moving daily. Otherwise, waste products and toxins stuck in the bowels will be reabsorbed from the intestines back into the blood stream, wreaking havoc on your health.

PROTOCOL FOR CONSTIPATION

In the case of constipation, what we remove from the diet is just as important as what we add. If the body cannot completely digest a food, elimination will be burdened and ineffective.

What to avoid or eliminate:

- Gluten: all wheat, barley, and rye flour products, breads, pastas, crackers, etc.

- Dairy products

- Black tea, including chai. Tea has a binding, astringent quality and is better used for loose stools or diarrhea

- Refined white foods: sugar, white rice, all flour products

- Cigarettes, alcohol, coffee, processed foods, and drug use will add heat to the system, drying out mucous membranes

Incorporate the following elements into your diet for healthier bowel function:

Moisture

- Most of us are mildly dehydrated, especially so in the mornings. First thing every morning, drink 16 ounces of warm water, adding the juice from half a lemon if desired.

- Drink half your body weight in ounces of water daily.

- Drink room-temperature liquids between meals, not with them. Drinking liquids with foods, especially cold or iced beverages, dilutes digestive enzymes and weakens digestion. A small amount of hot tea or broth may be consumed with meals.

- If you have dry skin or tend to be cold and tired, each morning drink a cup of hot herbal tea with 1 or 2 teaspoons of unrefined coconut oil added. Wait 30 minutes before eating breakfast.

- Eat soups and stews, which contain much-needed moisture and are easy to digest because of longer cooking times.

- Add one or more of these moistening foods to your daily diet: dark green leafy veggies, chlorella, coconut oil or milk, cooked prunes, spinach, sesame seed, millet, carrot, cauliflower, seaweed, pear, apple, almond, walnut, and oat or rice bran.

Magnesium

Magnesium is an essential mineral for many bodily functions, including elimination. Add foods rich in magnesium to your daily diet: dark, leafy greens (such as chard, kale or raw spinach), flax and pumpkin seeds, tahini (sesame butter), lentils, brown rice, avocado, banana, and dried figs.

Probiotics and Enzymes

To aid digestion and elimination, eat cultured or pickled foods such as sauerkraut, miso, kombucha, and kimchi. You may need to take a probiotic supplement to get enough of the beneficial bacteria to heal the gut. Yogurt simply does not provide enough probiotics, and if you are unable to digest dairy products completely, yogurt could add to digestive system problems.

Fiber

Fiber is an essential part of any healthy diet, as it binds with fat, cholesterol, excess hormones, and toxins in your intestines and speeds them through the digestive tract. Consume 30 to 50 grams of fiber daily for optimal health. For example, 1 cup of cooked black beans or lentils provides 15 grams of fiber. One tablespoon of chia seeds contains 10 grams of fiber.

- Eat whole foods every day to provide the fiber the body needs:
  Five to eight servings of fresh vegetables
  Two to three servings of beans or lentils
  One or two servings of fresh whole fruit (not juice)
  Two tablespoons chia, hemp, or ground flax seeds

- To heal the mucous membrane lining the intestines, soak 3 tablespoons of flax seeds for several hours or overnight and

drink. Do this once or twice daily until the bowels begin to
move smoothly by themselves.

Additional Suggestions

- Exercise is essential to get a sluggish elimination system
  moving. Begin a daily program of moderate exercise. For more
  on exercise, see the Wood Phase in part one.
- Consider getting acupuncture and an herbal formula from a
  nationally certified acupuncturist to balance Metal and help
  correct your constipation problems.

OPTIONAL SUPPLEMENTS

The following is a list of nutritional supplements that may be used
for constipation. Talk to your practitioner to see if any of these are
appropriate for you, or consult with a qualified herbalist to get a
customized herbal formula.

Nutritional supplements

Take 1000 mg combined of DHA/EPA one to two times
daily. See Appendices for more information on what to look
for in Omega-3 fatty acid supplements

Magnesium chelate:† 300 to 600 mg at bedtime. Begin with
300 mg nightly, adding an additional 300 mg if needed

Digestive enzymes: Take at each meal until constipation is
resolved

Daily probiotic supplement:‡ As per dosage instructions on
the label

Daily Cleanse Fiber or Supreme Cleanse by Gaia Herbs. As
per dosage instructions on the label

---

†I use Albion chelated minerals for optimal absorption such as those from Designs for Health.
‡ I prefer Culturelle, PB8, or Pharmax's HLC High Potency Capsules.

MOVING TOWARD BALANCE
IN THE WATER PHASE

Reminder: The challenge of the Water phase is to surrender to a time of dormancy and stillness. Sit in silence and listen deeply to access the wisdom stored within the unconscious. Be emptied of all striving, die to your old ways of being, and allow the deep well of being to replenish you.

ACTIONS

Begin incorporating rest into your life by scheduling unstructured downtime at least once per week.

Listen to a podcast or recording that addresses a topic that calls to a deep, perhaps unknown, part of yourself.

Retreat into contemplation or meditation for 20 minutes or longer each day.

GET CURIOUS ABOUT YOURSELF

What motivates you most strongly now? What can you do to engage your willpower to act on this?

What gives you a feeling of calm equanimity, of serenity? What can you do to feel this way more often?

What are you willing to do this week to incorporate one of the above actions into your daily life?

EATING TO BALANCE WATER

The Water phase corresponds with the season of winter. It is a time of downward movement, increasing cold, and storage of resources. Follow these eating guidelines to balance Water:

- Choose warm, nourishing food and drinks, especially in cold weather.
- Stews, soups, roasted root veggies, meats and nuts, and well cooked whole grains are good choices at this time.
- Cooked greens and winter squash, as well as black and kidney beans are beneficial.
- Cook foods longer and at lower temperatures.
- Drink a cup of warm water, broth, soup, or tea with each meal.
- Include small amounts of salty flavor foods such as miso, seaweeds, and gomasio.

THE KIDNEY AND ADRENAL HEALTH

The kidney is the yin organ of the Water phase. According to the classic texts of Oriental medicine, the kidney stores the jing, the precious and limited essence that is meant to last our entire life. Think of the stories of Zen masters who are still strong, vital, and mentally clear into very old age. This is our potential if we conserve and cultivate our jing. However, when we repeatedly push ourselves to excess with work, exercise, or consumption of any kind, we use up this limited essence. When we notice the consequences of this overdoing will depend on our individual constitution; some of us do not feel the effects until years after the excessive behaviors.

PROTOCOL FOR ADRENAL FATIGUE

The adrenal glands produce cortisol, a hormone that helps the body manage stress. Cortisol is released in response to fear or stress by the adrenals as part of the fight-or-flight mechanism. However, cortisol release is meant for emergencies and life-threatening situations, not for the everyday stresses of our demanding modern lives. When our bodies are in a constant state of stress, the natural rhythm of the adrenal glands becomes unbalanced, and the adrenals begin to secrete either too much or too little cortisol.

Symptoms of adrenal stress

- Strong cravings for sugar, carbs, or salt
- Mood swings; feeling agitated, anxious, irritated, fearful, or overwhelmed much of the time
- Fatigue with inability to stop and rest; "tired and wired"
- Racing thoughts, difficulty focusing on one thing at a time, mental fogginess
- High or low blood pressure (dizziness on standing can be a result of low blood pressure)
- Trouble falling or staying asleep; waking up exhausted

According to Oriental medicine, excess in any form depletes the energy stored in the kidney. It is essential to avoid life-depleting behaviors that overtax the adrenals on a daily basis. Closely observe the rhythm of your daily life, and notice when and what you are doing to excess. Make time to slow down and rest, especially when fatigued or ill. Never get so tired you feel you are on empty, with no reserves. Once you are depleted, it is more difficult to replenish.

Avoid the following adrenal stimulants:

- Sugars and simple carbohydrates
- Alcohol
- Caffeine, including all sodas, tea, chocolate, and decaffeinated coffee
- Excess exercise, work, socializing, eating, drinking, noise, activity
- Inadequate sleep

DAMAGE CONTROL

If you are going to eat sugar or other refined carbs, or drink caffeine or alcohol, be sure it is not on an empty stomach. First eat a meal or snack with protein and fat, which will slow down digestion and lessen the detrimental effects of the substances. For example, if you have a cup of green tea in the morning, fine. Just be sure you eat breakfast first. If you drink coffee, add some butter and/or coconut oil to it. It is surprisingly good! You'll find this one change will make a big difference in how you feel for the rest of the day.

LIFESTYLE GUIDELINES

- Do much less each day, saying no to nonessential activities.
- Schedule pauses in activity about every 90 minutes throughout the day. Take a few minutes to close your eyes and breathe deeply, walk around the office or yard, get a nutritious snack, glass of water, or cup of tea.
- Get adequate sleep, seven to nine hours every night. Consistently maintain your regular bedtime and wake-up hours, trying to be asleep by 10:30 p.m. every night, or earlier if possible.
- Avoid noisy or stressful distractions, computers, TV, and intense physical activity two to three hours before bedtime.

- Balance blood sugar. Eat a diet of whole, unprocessed foods consisting of vegetables, lean proteins, healthy fats, and small portions of whole grains. Please read Earth Protocol to Balance Blood Sugar for more details.

- Before bed, soak in a hot bath containing 2 cups Epsom salts, a half-cup baking soda, and 10 drops of lavender essential oil.

- Consider getting acupuncture and an herbal formula from a nationally certified acupuncturist to balance Water and help correct your adrenal fatigue.

- For more information, read *Adrenal Fatigue: The 21st Century Stress Syndrome* by James Wilson.

Helpful Practices

Take walks and do restorative or gentle yoga, tai chi, or qi gong to calm and strengthen the nervous system. Incorporating movement to gradually build your energy without pushing or depleting yourself is the goal.

Practice mindful breathing (see The ONE Thing in the Metal chapter in part one).

Adopt rhythmic moderation (see Earth practices in part one). Your hormones function best when you live in a rhythmic fashion, waking and sleeping at about the same time every day and having regular times for meals, exercise, and rest.

OPTIONAL SUPPLEMENTS

Talk to your practitioner to see if any of the following are appropriate for you, or consult with a qualified herbalist to get a customized herbal formula.

Nutritional Supplements

- *Eleuthero* or *American ginseng, Rhodiola, Cordyceps,* and *Ashwagandha* are some of the most common herbs for helping to balance adrenal and stress response

- *Adrenal Complex* and *Cortisol Manager* by Integrative Therapeutics and *Adrenal Health* by Gaia Herbs are products that support the adrenals without stimulants. Dosage as per label

- Take 1000 mg combined of DHA/EPA one to two times daily. See Appendices for more information on what to look for in Omega-3 fatty acid supplements

- Vitamin C: 500 to 1000 mg/day

- Zinc: 30 mg/day

- Vitamin B-50 complex:* Dosage as per label

---

*Spray or sublingual forms are the most easily absorbed.

STRESS AND HEALTH

Between 75 and 90 percent of all visits to primary care physicians involve stress-related complaints. Stress can have devastating effects on our health and sense of well being, so we cannot afford to ignore it. But many of us have no idea of the many factors that may underlie the stress we experience on a daily basis.

Stress is the way our body reacts to all the demands placed on us, both positive (such as a new relationship, job, or home) and negative (death, conflict, or illness). Either way, the body produces hormones to mediate the stress response, which suppress nonessential functions (e.g., digestion) and enhance others to help the body adapt (e.g., increased heart rate). This is what is known as the fight-or-flight response, when the whole body is geared up to react to get you through a crisis. For many of us, this response is triggered multiple times a day and on many levels, often unconsciously. Eventually the body does not know how to turn off the stress response, and we find ourselves in the unhappy state of chronic stress.

We generally are aware of certain obvious stress triggers—death in the family, divorce, moving, a new job. But there are unconscious triggers—repressed emotions, memories, viscerally held beliefs, past trauma—buried deep within, keeping the body in a state of chronic stress without our knowledge. This is a crucial distinction. If you do not know you are in distress, you are not likely to find effective ways to manage it. The body eventually responds to these unconscious triggers and may start to manifest symptoms of illness as a way to get our attention.

In his book, *When the Body Says No: Understanding the Stress–Disease Connection,* Dr. Gabor Maté shows that repressed emotion, over the long term, will generate enough physiologic stress to lower the immune response and create an environment that is conducive to disease. The stress connected with emotional repression is often overlooked and may lodge deep within the body. This is why it is essential for us to face the pain from past events as well as any repressed anger, resentment, and sadness we may have stored within us. Only then will the body be cleared, allowing us to be receptive to what life brings in the present moment.

Just Stress? Think Again

Patients frequently come to the clinic with a long list of complaints, such as insomnia, headaches, or pain, and then dismiss their symptoms by saying something like, "Oh, it's just stress." They are downplaying their own distress, effectively writing off their experience as something they have no control over. They may feel annoyed or even angry the body has let them down, forcing them to take time off from work or play to deal with this inconvenience. It is human nature to hope for a quick fix, an easy way out of suffering. This approach usually is not very helpful, however, and it does not get us what we need.

Doesn't it make more sense to stop for a moment and get curious about what the body is trying to say through its response to stress? You can choose to turn toward the body, toward your experience, and listen deeply to get to the root of your distress. It may take time and patient attention, but this book is here as a guide to help get you back into relationship with your body and your inner knowing.

Symptoms of stress may be mild or quite debilitating. Your personal history and emotional composition can directly influence what your body interprets as stress. When something happens in your life that connects in some way to your history, it can generate a stress response that is automatic, and often you are unaware of it.

What makes stress worse?

- Sedentary lifestyle
- Lack of purpose or of meaningful engagement in one's life
- Overstimulation and noise
- Intense exercise
- Environmental toxins
- Poor sleep
- Pain, surgery, accidents
- Anxiety, anger, sadness
- Ineffective communication within the family or at work
- Sugar, caffeine, alcohol
- Nutrient deficiency or metabolic dysfunction
- Repressed memory and emotion, unconsciously held beliefs

Notice how the causes of stress go both ways in the above list: If you are either too sedentary or overstimulated, your stress will get worse. This speaks to the belief in Oriental medicine that the foundation of good health is finding a balance of yin and yang in your relationships and behaviors.

REDUCE STRESS, STABILIZE ENERGY AND MOOD

Now the good news: Research shows that the harmful effects of stress are not inevitable. For one thing, the way we think about stress determines its effects on the body. If we view our response to stress as beneficial for our performance, we'll be less anxious about a pounding heart or faster breathing. With this broader perspective, we will be more relaxed, and the body will not react as if there is a problem. Again, mind and body are not separate entities; they are one and the same. This can work for us or against us, depending on our level of awareness.

For most of us, some form of daily stress is inevitable. In addition to understanding the roots of stress, it is essential we take concrete steps to reduce its impact on our health.

LIFESTYLE GUIDELINES

- Get adequate sleep, seven to nine hours every night. Consistently maintain your regular bedtime and wake-up hours.

- Avoid caffeine after lunch, and avoid alcohol, noisy or stressful distractions, use of computers, TV, and intense physical activity two hours before bedtime.

- Exercise regularly, in the outdoors with natural light if possible. Thirty minutes of moderate activity on a daily basis is sufficient for most people.

- Surround yourself with music, art, nature, or a hobby you enjoy. Garden, volunteer, make new connections through an activity or community that engages you.

- Balance blood sugar. Eat a diet of whole, unprocessed foods consisting of vegetables, lean proteins, healthy fats, and small portions of whole grains. Please read Earth Protocol to Balance Blood Sugar for a detailed discussion of this topic.

- Have regular acupuncture treatments. Research shows acupuncture reduces the level of stress hormones in the blood.

- Practice what most calms you: mindful breathing, gardening, guided imagery tapes, or yoga.

- Try this bath before bed: Soak for 20 minutes or more in a hot bath containing 2 cups Epsom salts, a half-cup baking soda, and 10 drops of lavender essential oil.

- Read Dr. Gabor Maté's book, *When The Body Says No: Understanding the Stress–Disease Connection.*

What To Avoid

Sugar and other simple carbohydrates: pasta, bread, white rice, chips, cookies, bagels, etc.

Alcohol

Caffeine, especially on an empty stomach or after noon. Green tea is okay for most people.

Excess in any form: too much exercise, work, partying, eating, drinking, or stimulation

Being too sedentary or not engaged in life

OPTIONAL SUPPLEMENTS

Talk to your practitioner to see if any of the following are appropriate for you, or consult with a qualified herbalist to get a customized herbal formula.

Nutritional Supplements

Rhodiola rosea, 100 mg 2 to 3 times daily between meals for several months*

Cortisol Manager by Integrative Therapeutics helps calm the stress response and aids sleep

Take 1000 mg combined of DHA/EPA one to two times daily. See Appendices for more information on what to look for in Omega-3 fatty acid supplements

Magnesium chelate:† 300 mg/day

L-theanine:‡ 200 mg, 1 to 4 times daily depending on your stress level

Vitamin C: 500 to 1000 mg/day

Zinc: 30 mg/day

Vitamin B-50 complex: 2 tablets/day

---

* *Rhodiola* may be combined with *Ashwagandha* and *Eleuthero ginseng*, as all three of these herbs help the body adapt to stress.

†I use Albion chelated minerals for optimal absorption as those found in Designs for Health.

‡Look for products containing Suntheanine, a proprietary L-theanine extract

NUTRITION BASICS FOR ALL PHASES

Here is some common sense nutrition advice to serve as a foundation for maintaining good health in all phases. Refer to this chapter for information on the whole foods diet, the correct types of fats to eat, and the importance of protein, as well as lists of foods to incorporate in your daily diet and foods to avoid or eliminate altogether. To help ease the transition to a whole foods diet, at the end of the chapter I have provided some simple menu suggestions for healthy meals and snacks.

THE DIET-HEALTH CONNECTION

The old cliché is true: You are what you eat. The food you ingest becomes the physical building blocks for your tissues. Our bodies are constantly regenerating on a cellular level, which is good news for us. We are changing all the time. This is why it is of utmost importance to feed the body the best quality food possible. You probably fill your car with quality gasoline; why not fill your own body with quality fuel? Many patients have told me this perspective made the idea of change interesting to them, rather than a burden. They became curious about the body in a new way as they experimented with what was the best fuel for their unique metabolism.

Serious illnesses such as cancer, diabetes, and heart disease, as well as fatigue, hormonal disruption, anxiety, sleep disturbances, bowel disorders, and pain conditions are all influenced by what we eat. In 1988, Surgeon General Dr. C. Everett Koop pointed to the standard American diet as the cause of approximately two-thirds of deaths due to disease in the United States. This should come as no surprise.

Most Americans eat very little, if any, of the fresh vegetables, fruits, high quality fats, and whole grains that are essential for health. Instead, we tend to eat more sugar in one week than Americans ate in one year 200 years ago. We also consume an excess of processed and packaged foods, which generally do not provide adequate nutrition.

The good news is that in most cases, we can easily improve or prevent these ailments without pills or surgery. All we need to do is pay more attention to what we consume.

WHY FAT MATTERS

There is a common belief in our culture that dietary fat is bad and must be avoided for good health. Fat, especially saturated fat, has been erroneously associated for decades with weight gain, high cholesterol, and heart disease. It is time we recognize that our overconsumption of sugar, simple carbohydrates, and refined vegetable oils, compounded by eating fewer quality fats, is the main factor behind the current obesity, diabetes, and cardiovascular epidemics.

Nutritionists now understand that eating the *right* kind of fat is essential for optimal health. But too many people refuse to eat any fat at all, especially animal fat. Most of my patients who limit their fat consumption experience one or more of the following: gas, bloating, constipation, fatigue, difficulty concentrating, dry or rough skin, intolerance of cold, anxiety, insomnia, and difficulty regulating weight.

The fact is, if you are not eating a diet of whole foods—which most of us are not—and you eliminate fat from your diet, your body is going to suffer from a lack of essential nutrients. One of two scenarios may develop:

1. You will graze, and eat, and eat more until the body gets the nutrients it needs. In the process you will consume too many calories and too much sugar, salt, and trans fats from processed foods.

2. You will rigidly try to control your appetite through dieting, exercise, cleanses, and consumption of stimulants (such as sugar and caffeine) instead of eating whole foods and fats to give your body the nutrients it craves.

My clinical experience has shown me the extremes of these two common dietary mistakes: patients who are overweight and fatigued, and those who are thin and anxious. Neither makes any sense for long-term health and happiness. Remember the wisdom of the Earth phase, which asks us to practice moderation in all things.

For many years, mainstream nutritionists and the media have urged us to avoid full fat in the foods we buy, including dairy products. Widely available low-fat and fat-free foods are highly processed products that replace the flavor that comes from fat with sugar or artificial sweeteners, which weaken the Earth phase and disrupt blood sugar regulation. The most beneficial product is the whole product, with all its parts intact, including the fat. However, consumption of dairy products should be limited for most people. Like meat, dairy can be regarded as a side dish to your meal, not its center.

From the perspective of Oriental medicine, fats are one of the most yin substances in your diet. They are heavy, slow, and dense. (You can see why a culture like ours, which rewards light, fast, and sleek, would create a defense against fat.) Fats satisfy your taste buds, allow you to feel full, and help you get grounded. In *Healing With Whole Foods,* Paul Pitchford states, "Fats build the tissues, enhance fluid metabolism, and direct nutrients into the nervous system. Then the predominantly yin aspect of fat gradually changes into a yang, physically energizing, and warming quality. This is why fats are so highly valued—people like to feel secure, to slow down, and to have ample energy and warmth."

I encourage all my patients to eat the right kind of fats, such as those found in a whole foods diet, to maintain weight, energy, and health. Suggestions on incorporating healthy fats in your diet can be found below in the discussion on daily nutrition.

WHOLE FOODS AND COOKING

Whole food is food that has not been tinkered with and changed. The fat has not been removed; no sugar, vitamins, chemicals, preservatives, or genetically modified organisms (GMOs) have been added. This is food in its original state, the way nature, in her wisdom, created it. It is the kind of food that will spoil if left out on the counter and not eaten promptly.

Most of us do not have an unlimited shopping budget, so why waste your money on foods that do not enhance your health? The next time you go to the grocery store, notice where the whole food is, the food your great grandparents would recognize. Generally, the outer periphery of the store is where you want to shop. This is where you will find the fresh fruits and vegetables, the full-fat dairy, real butter, whole eggs, poultry, fish, and grass-fed meat. Now walk the center aisles. This is where you will find highly processed and refined food products that are generally detrimental to your health. Even in so-called health food stores, hundreds of these packaged products line the shelves. Read the ingredient lists on products you normally buy and decide if this is what you want in your body. Would this have been considered food by your great grandparents? If not, think twice before consuming it. And remember the 80/20 rule: if you are not experiencing any imbalances, you may be able to enjoy some of these foods on occasion without negative side effects.

Cooking has become a spectator sport for many of us, something we watch accomplished chefs do on television. Instead of cooking simple, nourishing, and delicious meals, we buy packaged or frozen foods, or get take-out or prepared foods from the store. This is fine now and then, but we need to get back into cooking to be whole and healthy. Cooking gives you so much more than physical health, as important as that is. Cooking your own food is a simple and fundamental way to nourish and love yourself. Cooking and sharing a meal with others can add love, warmth, and companionship to your life.

Cooking is also an essential way to engage in the rhythmic cycle of life, as you stop what you are doing and focus your attention on preparing nourishment. It gives the psyche a positive message: Yes, I value myself enough to take time to nourish my body. Cooking also gets you in touch with the alchemical process of using heat and water to change raw ingredients into life-sustaining food. You don't need to slave over a hot stove for hours to reap the benefits of cooking whole foods. You can prepare simple meals with fresh ingredients, and make it fun by inviting others to cook with you and share recipes, techniques, and good conversation.

You have the freedom to make choices for transformation in your life. Ask yourself: What do I really need for a vital and healthy body? What would truly nourish me? Watch for the things you habitually want. Do not give in to the mistaken belief that a strong desire for something means you need it. Remember, you literally are what you eat.

Why Local and Organic?

Buying locally grown food promotes eating fresh and in season, saves transport costs and fossil fuels, and benefits local economies. With this one choice, you take care of your body as well as the precious earth that sustains us all. Buying organic is especially important with animal-based foods such as meats, eggs, and dairy. Conventionally raised animals are treated with high doses of hormones and antibiotics, and these substances are concentrated in the fat portion of the food. If you think organic foods are expensive, just remember the savings in future health care costs you are gaining by eating foods that actually nourish you. Also, by following the guidelines presented here, you will find yourself eating less because the food is more nutrient-dense and satisfying. However, if local or organic is not an option for you, not to worry. Simply buy the freshest, least processed foods available and you will reap the benefits.

PROTEIN IS ESSENTIAL

Adequate protein is essential to good health, but many of us get too much and others not nearly enough. Protein requirements vary depending on physical activity, stress, and constitution. The amount of protein you ingest, however, is only part of the equation. Another factor is the bioavailability of the protein you consume, or what your body is able to digest and assimilate. Animal foods are the only sources of protein that contain all nine essential amino acids, making them the most bioavailable sources of protein for most people. If you lack digestive enzymes or you eat foods your body cannot fully metabolize, you will not be able to use the protein in a particular food. The most common foods my patients have difficulty digesting are soy, wheat, dairy, corn, peanuts, grains, and beans.

Dietary choices are often very personal. I simply ask you to observe how your body responds to your current eating habits and be open to listening to what the body needs, rather than what the mind demands. For example, a vegetarian diet works very well for some of my patients. They take the time to cook and eat a variety of freshly prepared plant foods and are healthy, vital people. However, I have other patients determined to follow a strict vegetarian or vegan diet even when it is not working for them. They report being frequently sick, tired, or cold, and can often trace these symptoms back to when they took animal foods out of their diet. When they begin to consume small amounts of these foods again, their bodies respond, symptoms resolve, and they feel much better. (See appendices for an easy method for calculating protein needs.)

HEALTHY FOOD CHOICES

A great deal of information on nutrition is now available, and it seems everyone believes their way is the only way. However, each of us is biochemically unique, and it should make sense that no one way to eat will work for everyone. I have learned that extreme dietary choices do not enhance long-term health. Dietary needs change depending on health, activity, stress, age, and environment, so it is wise to not hold too rigidly to any one way of eating.

Consider the common sense wisdom of Oriental dietary therapy: Eat according to the seasons and the current needs of your body and lifestyle, while addressing any imbalances you may be experiencing.

For example, if you live where it is very warm and your digestion is strong, eating more raw vegetables and fruit is fine. At times of increased activity or in cold weather, including more fat and protein is appropriate. Trust yourself and your body's response to foods. Use moderation and common sense when choosing foods, observe the results, and you will learn what works for you.

From my experience, it takes at least 30 days of constant repetition to establish a new routine. Don't beat yourself up if you find yourself off the wagon and back to your old eating habits. Change takes determination and patience, especially when we are trying to change long-held beliefs, attitudes, and behaviors.

Unprocessed, whole foods should make up the bulk of your daily diet. If you follow these guidelines most of the time, with only occasional exceptions, your energy, mood, and overall health will improve.

Fresh Vegetables. Eat a variety of colorful veggies, being sure to include seasonal ones. These should be mostly cooked but some may be raw, especially in spring and summer.

Fresh Fruit. Eat a variety of seasonal fruit, more in summer and in warmer climates, less when it is cold or your digestion is weak. Cook fruit in cooler weather. Keep to one to two servings daily of low glycemic fruit such as berries if you have a blood sugar imbalance.

Grains. Choose brown and wild rice, barley, steel-cut oats, amaranth, quinoa, and millet.

Animal foods. Include free range eggs, lean poultry, beef, elk, bison, pork, and lamb, as well as wild caught fish when available. In colder climates and in the winter, the body will welcome more meats and fats. Eat less animal foods in warmer climates and in the summer.

Cultured foods. Add sauerkraut, miso, pickles, kombucha, kimchi.

Legumes. Eat lentils and beans of all kinds, as well as hummus (chick pea spread).

Nuts and seeds. Include walnuts, almonds, pecans, pumpkin, sunflower, chia, hemp, and flax seeds.

Dairy. Choose organic and full-fat plain yogurt, cheese, and butter. Soft goat and feta cheeses are good options.

Oils and fats. Use extra virgin, cold-pressed olive oil, butter, ghee (clarified butter), unrefined coconut oil, as well as avocado, nuts and seeds, animal foods, and full fat dairy products.

Spices and herbs. Add warming spices such as cinnamon, cloves, ginger, and pepper when it is cold, and cooling ones such as parsley, cilantro, dill, basil, and mint in the summer. Use Celtic sea salt or other natural salt with the minerals intact, not processed, iodized salt.

Drinks. Drink spring water, herbal teas, grain coffees, green tea, and spritzers made with fruit juice mixed with mineral water. Black tea or coffee occasionally may be okay for some people.

Seaweeds. Add kombu or wakame to soups, beans, and grains while they are cooking to increase the mineral content and make them more digestible.

FOODS TO AVOID

The following foods may increase the body's susceptibility to illness and should be eaten sparingly if at all.

Processed and packaged foods. This includes breads, bagels, chips, soft drinks, cereals, pastries, crackers, muffins, pasta. The use of some canned and frozen foods is fine.

Caffeine. Avoid coffee (including decaf), black tea, and chai, especially on an empty stomach. Green tea is usually mild enough for most people.

Alcohol. Keep to one drink per day if you do drink.

Sugars. Avoid white or brown sugar, agave, honey, maple syrup, etc. Use small amounts of stevia to sweeten if needed.

Soy. Modern soy products are highly processed and genetically modified and contain substances that may cause digestive, thyroid, and immune system dysfunction. Small amounts of whole or fermented soy foods—edamame, miso, tamari—are okay.

FOODS TO ELIMINATE

Always read labels, with a goal of eliminating the following substances:

High-fructose corn syrup. HFCS has been shown to contribute to the development of obesity and type 2 diabetes.

Artificial sweeteners. Watch out for aspartame (NutraSweet, Equal), sucralose (Splenda), saccharine (Sweet'n Low), and sorbitol.

Trans fats. Hydrogenated and partially hydrogenated oils are found in fast foods, margarine, and most commercially produced baked goods, such as crackers, breads, and cookies.

Monosodium glutamate (MSG) and other food additives are found in numerous prepared foods. If it sounds like you need a chemistry lab to make it, you probably want to avoid it.

Soft drinks, including diet soft drinks. The sugar, HFCS, or artificial sweeteners they contain are all extremely detrimental to health.

GMOs. This includes most products made with corn, soy, or canola oil.

Vegetable and seed oils. Corn, soy, sunflower, and canola oils are highly processed. Cold-pressed olive oil is a much better choice.

Wheat products. Modern wheat has been so genetically altered that it is difficult to digest. It is not only a question of gluten intolerance; modern wheat is also high glycemic.

Salad Dressing

Most prepared salad dressings use corn, soy, or canola oils as well as sugar and other undesirable ingredients. Making your own is simple: use a 2:1 ratio of oil to vinegar. In a glass jar with a lid, put in 1 cup olive oil and a half-cup total of red wine vinegar, balsamic vinegar, and/or lemon juice. Add mustard and herbs if you like. Shake well. Does not need to be refrigerated.

OTHER CONSIDERATIONS

- Eat plenty of high-fiber foods. Fiber binds with fat, cholesterol, excess hormones, and toxins in your intestines and speeds them through the digestive tract and out of your body. Fiber also helps the body burn more calories and reduces appetite by helping you stay full longer.

- Add foods that enhance the growth of beneficial intestinal flora, including cooked greens, wheat grass, yogurt, and fermented foods such as sauerkraut, kombucha, kefir, and miso.

- Eat mindfully, bringing your whole self to the meal. Explore all areas of your life to find additional sources of nourishment (spiritual, creative, or social, for example), so that food does not carry the entire burden of sustaining you.

- Note that too much cold or raw food and drink will weaken digestion. Include soups, well-cooked grains, and baked or steamed veggies in your daily diet. Drink warm or room-temperature fluids, especially if it is cold out or your digestion is already weak (i.e., gas or bloating, fatigue, tired after eating, overweight, sluggish). Salads and fresh fruits are more appropriate in the warmer months. Iced drinks and ice cream will weaken the digestive fire and thus the entire body. Eat ice cream and other frozen treats (even the nonfat variety) sparingly and infrequently.

- Balanced blood sugar is essential in all phases. Observe how many carbohydrates you are consuming and how that relates to your energy level and overall well being. See Earth Protocol to Balance Blood Sugar for more information.

- Take 1000 mg combined of DHA/EPA one to two times daily to provide the essential fatty acids (EFAs) the body needs. See Appendices for more information on what to look for in Omega-3 fatty acid supplements.

- For some people, avoiding or eliminating gluten (wheat, barley, rye, oats, spelt, kamut, triticale) or dairy products (milk, cheese, butter, yogurt) is essential to restore and maintain good health.

- If you suspect you may have food allergies, the most common allergens to avoid are wheat, dairy, eggs, corn, soy, peanuts, citrus, nightshade plants (tomatoes, eggplant, peppers, potatoes), and yeasted products (wine, vinegar, breads).

MENU SUGGESTIONS TO KEEP IT SIMPLE

Below are some meal suggestions to show you that adopting a new way of eating does not have to be complicated or time consuming. Open your mind to the idea of eating soups and vegetables for breakfast the way people do in Asian nations. Soups and congee strengthen the digestion and give you a nutrient-rich way to begin the day. Congee can be such a useful addition to your diet that I have included a simple recipe with some tasty variations in the appendices.

Breakfast

Eating a breakfast with protein and good quality fats (and little, if any, simple carbohydrates) is essential to nourish you and stabilize your energy and mood throughout the day. Research has shown that those who eat a breakfast like this enjoy better overall health and are able to lose weight and maintain weight loss much better than those who skip breakfast.

Try some of the following

- Cheese or avocado on rice crackers

- Plain, sugar-free yogurt with fresh fruit, flax or pumpkin seeds, walnuts, or almonds

- Eggs with greens or other fresh vegetables

- Quick morning porridge: Add 1 cup boiling water to 2 tablespoons each of hemp seed, chia seed, and unsweetened coconut milk. Stir well and add fresh blueberries or other fruit. Let sit for five minutes before eating. Adjust the amount of water to get desired consistency

- Congee made with whole grains such as steel-cut oats, brown rice, or millet with butter or nuts added for fat (see congee recipe in the appendices)

- Dinner for breakfast: salmon with vegetables or a hearty chicken vegetable soup.

- For lighter fare in warm weather, occasionally have a protein shake (not soy-based), almond butter on an apple, or fruit and nuts

Lunch and Dinner

Fill at least half your plate with your favorite vegetables—mostly cooked, some raw, or as soup or salad. Add one serving of lean animal or other protein at each of these meals. Include beans and legumes frequently. You may include well-cooked, whole grains if you like. Some people do well with no grains at all and eat small servings of sweet potatoes or cauliflower "mashed potatoes" instead.

Suggestions

- Chicken and vegetable soup, with added brown rice if desired

- Mixed veggie salad with hummus, avocado, and nuts with spilt pea soup

- Fried eggs on a bed of black beans, topped with salsa and avocado

- Lentil and veggie soup

- Quiche or veggie omelet with salad or soup

- Grilled chicken or salmon with steamed veggies and quinoa

- Baked chicken with roasted carrots, onions, and sweet potatoes; sautéed broccoli

Snacks

- Walnuts, almonds, sunflower or pumpkin seeds

- Almond butter or tahini (sesame butter) on apples, celery, or rice crackers

- Raw veggies with hummus or guacamole

- Sugar-free, full-fat yogurt or kefir with fresh fruit

- Cheese with sliced turkey or hard-boiled egg

- Protein shakes blended with freshly ground flaxseed or almonds and unsweetened coconut milk, with a touch of cinnamon and vanilla added if desired

A Word on Blenders and Bars

Throwing protein powder, fruits, veggies, and supplements into a blender or eating a protein bar is not the same thing as eating a meal of whole foods. When we consider that raw or cold foods and concentrated protein powders may be difficult to digest and that many fruits contain a lot of sugar, it makes sense that we should consume them in moderation. If you need to eat them now and then, no problem, but they should not be a part of your daily diet.

Some tips for making shakes: Choose low-glycemic fruits such as berries, include generally more veggies than fruits, and use unsweetened coconut or almond milk rather than fruit juice or ice. Drink a cup of hot water or ginger tea to balance the cold and raw nature of the shake. It is certainly better to have a nutrient-dense shake than to skip a meal or eat junk food, but don't rely on blenders and bars to meet your nutritional needs too often. Warm, cooked, whole foods have a calming effect and nourish us deeply on many levels.

A Note on Raw Food

The raw food diet has many proponents, based on the idea that many nutrients are lost in the process of cooking. However, one must consider the actual bioavailability of nutrients in food in both raw and cooked forms. While there may be a higher concentration of nutrients in raw foods, the nutrients are not necessarily available to the body because raw foods can be hard to digest. Cooked foods, on the other hand, may have lost some nutrients through heating, but the body can easily digest the remaining nutrients. Therefore, the net amount of digested and thus useful nutrients is higher in cooked foods. Consuming more raw foods is appropriate in warm weather.

PART THREE

RESOURCES

APPENDICES

OMEGA-3 FATTY ACIDS

Omega-3s are essential fatty acids, or EFAs, and are essential for optimal health. EFAs have been shown to significantly benefit cardiac, neurological, and cognitive function, reduce symptoms of ADHD and Alzheimer's disease, alleviate inflammation and thus relieve both joint pain and asthma, as well as positively impact hormonal balance, and mood disorders such as depression and anxiety.

The body cannot produce EFAs, so we must get them through our diet. Two crucial ones, EPA and DHA, are primarily found in certain fish. To consume a therapeutic dose that will provide the above benefits, I recommend all my patients take the following:

- 1000 mg combined EPA/DHA one to two times daily, with food.

Note: Many discount suppliers sell products labeled "1000 mg fish oil." This is not what you want. The label should state: 1000mg combined EPA and DHA. For example: 600 mg EPA and 400 mg DHA per two capsules, or similar amounts that total 1000 mg of EPA and DHA.

Use high-quality fish oil supplied by your practitioner or from a trustworthy manufacturer, such as Ultimate Omega by Nordic Naturals or OmegAvail Ultra from Designs for Health, or other similar product.

HOW MUCH PROTEIN?

Calculating Protein Needs (in Grams)

Adults: Multiply ideal healthy weight (not actual current weight) by 0.36. (For example, a woman who should weigh 120 pounds needs about 43 grams of protein a day (120 x 0.36 = 43.2). You can simplify the calculation by estimating one-third your ideal healthy weight (in the example given, this would be approximately 40 pounds) and aiming to consume a similar number of grams of protein a day.

For Children: Simplify the calculation of 0.55 by estimating one half the child's ideal body weight and making sure he or she gets a similar number of grams of protein a day. For a child whose ideal healthy weight is 60 pounds, this would be approximately 30 grams of protein daily.

Protein content of common foods

One egg: 6 grams

Almonds (1 ounce or 2 tablespoons butter): 6 grams

Cottage cheese (one half cup): 13 grams

Cheese (one ounce): 9 grams

Greek yogurt (1 cup): 14 grams

Black beans (1 cup cooked): 14 grams

Brown rice (1 cup cooked): 5 grams

Chicken breast (3 ounces):* 17 grams

Salmon (3 ounces): 22 grams

---

*A 3–4 ounce portion of animal protein is about the size of a deck of cards.

RECIPES

Congee

Here is a simple recipe for congee, a thin, easily digested Oriental grain soup, usually made with rice and eaten as breakfast porridge. For those who want to enhance their digestion, congee can be eaten as a part of any meal. The long cooking time required breaks down the grain, making it very easy to digest and assimilate the nutrients it contains.

The traditional recipe has only two ingredients, rice and water. Play with the proportions of water to grain until you get the consistency that satisfies you the most. See below for suggested ingredients to add to make savory and sweet variations of the basic recipe.

Basic Congee

1 cup rice or other grain

6 to 8 cups water

Use only clay, enamel, glass, or stainless steel cookware to make congee. Do not use iron or aluminum pots, as these may leach unwanted metals into your food.

On the stovetop: Heat water to a slow boil in a covered pot. Add grain to boiling water. Bring to a slow boil again and reduce heat to the lowest setting on your stove. Cover and cook approximately four hours, until the grain is well dissolved in the liquid.

In a crockpot or slow cooker: Heat water to a slow boil on high temperature (this will take about an hour). Add grain to boiling water. Cover, bring to a slow boil again, then reduce heat to low. Cook all day or overnight.

For a Savory Congee

- To the cooked plain congee, add leftover cooked meat, greens, veggies, or boiled eggs and serve with gomasio (see below for recipe).

- You may use any combination of grain, veggies, meat, and spices you like. One tasty combination is rice, celery, onion, bay leaf, and one or two bone-in chicken thighs. Place all ingredients in pot and cook together as directed in the basic recipe.

To Make Sweet Congee

- To the cooked plain congee, add cooked or dried fruit, butter or ghee, cinnamon, and a teaspoon of honey or maple syrup.

- Combine any grain, veggies or fruits, nuts, and spices you like. I like millet, carrots, cinnamon and cloves cooked together as directed in the basic recipe.

Gomasio (sesame salt condiment)

2 cups sesame seeds

1 tablespoon Celtic sea salt

Combine ingredients and roast for 10 minutes in iron skillet over medium heat, stirring constantly with a wooden spoon until seeds turn golden brown. Grind into a coarse meal in a mortar and pestle. Store in glass container in the fridge for up to six weeks.

HOME TREATMENT FOR THE COMMON COLD

- Drink room temperature or warm water, and be sure to stay hydrated by drinking one half your body weight in ounces of water daily.

- If you have a sore throat, gargle with warm salt water. My patients and I have used this technique for years and it really works! Add honey to hot tea to soothe the throat. Suck on zinc lozenges.

- Drink water mixed with one-half teaspoon baking soda once or twice daily to help alkalinize the body quickly.

- Make rest a priority.

- Use a neti pot for nasal irrigation.

- Eat only easy-to-digest, cooked and warm foods in small quantities (soups, porridge, congee, stews).

- Avoid cold drinks, cold and raw foods, heavy meats, greasy foods, sugar, dairy, and wheat.

- Keep a humidifier running, especially at night in the bedroom, to keep the airways moist.

How to "Sweat it Out"

Make a tea that will help you sweat: In a glass or enamel pot, add six to eight slices of raw ginger and three to four cloves of raw garlic to 2 1/2 cups of water. Bring to a boil, reduce heat, cover, and simmer lightly for 15 minutes. Strain. Add honey if you have a sore throat. Drink one cup.

Prepare the bathroom to make it very warm, with no drafts of cold air. Have warm, dry clothes ready. Soak in a very hot bath while drinking another cup of your hot tea until you feel very hot, at least 10 to 15 minutes.

When ready, get out, dry yourself, and put on warm clothes before going to bed and lying down, covering yourself in blankets (wool, if available). Cover your neck and head. Allow no drafts to get to you while your pores are so open. Lie down for about 20 to 30 minutes and sweat.

Afterwards, put on dry, warm clothes, covering your neck and head well. Do not go outside or expose yourself to wind or cold. If you have been able to sweat, you will soon feel much better, but continue to rest one more day. If you did not sweat, try one more time the next day.

If your symptoms become severe or enter the lungs, with a heavy chest and deep cough, it is best to consult your practitioner and get treatment with acupuncture and herbal medicine. Letting symptoms linger or go deeper into the body will weaken the system and make the illness more difficult to resolve.

Add one or more of the following for treatment:

Yin Qiao San: Take at the first signs of a cold or sore throat. Follow dosage instructions on label.

Gan Mao Ling: Take 4 to 8 tablets every two to three hours (or as directed on label) with hot water. This powerful antiviral formula is for warm-type viral infections, so use only if there are signs of heat (fever, elevated pulse, red or sore throat).

Oscillococcinum: One capful (not the whole vial) every three hours. Allow to dissolve in mouth.

RECOMMENDED RESOURCES

Finding a Practitioner of Oriental Medicine

National Certification Commission for Acupuncture and Oriental Medicine

www.NCCAOM.org

The NCCAOM is the national commissioning board that certifies acupuncturists and herbalists in the US.

People's Organization of Community Acupuncture

www.pocacoop.com

POCA is a national organization representing the community acupuncture movement, which provides low-cost acupuncture treatments in a group setting.

For Nutritional Supplements and Traditional Chinese Herbal Formulas

Whole Foods Market

Pharmaca Integrated Pharmacy

www.thenaturalonline.com

The following are some of the many providers of high quality supplements: Designs for Health, Standard Process, Integrated Therapeutics, Gaia Herbs, Pure Encapsulations, Klaire Labs, Thorne, Enzymatic Therapy, and Natural Factors.

I recommend Golden Flower, Herbal Times, and Plum Flower brand herbs, or consult with your practitioner for a customized herbal formula.

Nutrition

Prescription for Nutritional Healing by Phyllis A. Balch

Wheat Belly by William Davis, MD

Sugar Blues by William Dufty

The Blood Sugar Solution by Mark Hyman, MD

The UltraMind Solution: Fix Your Brain by Healing Your Body First by Mark Hyman, MD

Healing with Whole Foods: Oriental Traditions and Modern Nutrition by Paul Pitchford

Practical Paleo: A Customized Approach to Health and a Whole Foods Lifestyle by Diane Sanfilippo, BS, NC

The Metabolic Typing Diet by William L. Wolcott and Trish Fahey

Psychology and Soul Work

The End of Your World: Uncensored Straight Talk on the Nature of Enlightenment by Adyashanti

Knowing Woman: A Feminine Psychology by Irene Claremont de Castillejo

When Things Fall Apart: Heart Advice for Difficult Times by Pema Chodron

Shamanic Journeying: A Beginners Guide by Sandra Ingerman

Inner Work by Robert A. Johnson (Describes the use of active imagination with dreams)

Memories, Dreams, and Reflections by Carl G. Jung

Culture and ideology are not your friends, Opening the doors of creativity, and many more on youtube.com or as podcasts on Psychedelic Salon by Terence McKenna

The Practice of Wholeness by Lorena Monda

Zen Flesh Zen Bones: A Collection of Zen and Pre-Zen Writings by Paul Reps and Nyogen Senzaki

The Essential Rumi: New Expanded Edition by Jalal al-Din Rumi (translated by Coleman Barks and John Moyne)

Bond with the Beloved by Llewellyn Vaughan-Lee

Love is a Fire: The Sufi's Mystical Journey Home by Llewellyn Vaughan-Lee

Addiction to Perfection: The Still Unravished Bride by Marion Woodman

The Crown of Age by Marion Woodman (AudioBook CD)

Taoism

Tao Te Ching by Lao Tsu (translated by Gia-Fu Feng and Jane English)

I Ching or The Book of Changes (translated by Richard Wilhelm and Cary Baynes)

Other

Change or Die: The Three Keys to Change at Work and in Life by Alan Deutschman

Younger Next Year by Chris Crowley and Henry S. Lodge, MD

When The Body Says No: Exploring the Stress–Disease Connection by Gabor Maté, MD

Nonviolent Communication: A Language of Life by Marshall B. Rosenberg

Adrenal Fatigue: The 21st Century Stress Syndrome by James L. Wilson, MD

REFERENCES

Adyashanti. 2008. *The End of Your World: Uncensored Straight Talk on the Nature of Enlightenment.* Boulder, CO: Sounds True, Incorporated.

Brown, Brené. *"The Power of Vulnerability."* Presented at TEDx Houston, TX, June 2010.

Davis, William. 2011. *Wheat Belly.* New York: Rodale, Inc.

Deutschman, Alan. 2007. *Change or Die: The Three Keys to Change at Work and in Life.* New York: Harper Collins Publishers.

Gia-Fu Feng and Jane English, trans. 1972. *Tao Te Ching* by Lao Tsu. New York: Vintage Books.

Hanh, Thich Nhat. 1987. *Being Peace.* Berkeley: Parallax Press.

Maté, Gabor. 2003. *When The Body Says No: Exploring the Stress–Disease Connection.* Hoboken, NJ: John Wiley and Sons.

McKenna, Terence. *Culture and ideology are not your friends, Opening the doors of creativity, and more.* Podcasts available on Psychedelic Salon.

Pitchford, Paul. 1993. *Healing with Whole Foods: Oriental Traditions and Modern Nutrition.* Berkeley: North Atlantic Books

Reps, Paul and Nyogen Senzaki. 1998. Zen Flesh, Zen Bones: *A Collection of Zen and Pre-Zen Writings.* Boston, Rutland, VT, Tokyo: Tuttle Publishing. First published in 1957.

Vaughan-Lee, Llewelyn. *Personal communication,* May 2001.

Vaughan-Lee, Llewelyn. *"About Oneness." Working With Oneness* website, accessed November 8, 2013, http://workingwithoneness.org.

BIBLIOGRAPHY

Oriental Medicine And Philosophy

Gia Fu and Jane English, trans. 1972. *Tao Te Ching* by Lao Tsu. New York: Vintage Books.

Jarrett, Lonny S. 1998. *Nourishing Destiny: The Inner Tradition of Chinese Medicine.* Stockbridge, MA.: Spirit Path Press.

Kaptchuk, Ted. 1983. *The Web That Has No Weaver.* New York: Congdon & Weed. Distributed by St. Martin's Press.

Maciocia, Giovanni. 1989. *The Foundations of Chinese Medicine.* Edinburgh; New York: Churchill Livingstone.

Chinese Dietary Therapy and Modern Nutrition

Davis, William. 2011. *Wheat Belly.* New York: Rodale, Inc.

Flaws, Bob and Honora Wolfe. 1983. *Prince Wen Hui's Cook: Chinese Dietary Therapy.* Brookline, MA: Paradigm Publications.

Hyman, Mark. 2010. *The UltraMind Solution: Fix Your Brain by Healing Your Body First.* New York: Scribner.

Pitchford, Paul. 1993. *Healing with Whole Foods: Oriental Traditions and Modern Nutrition.* Berkeley: North Atlantic Books.

Wolcott, William L. and Trish Fahey. 2000. *The Metabolic Typing Diet.* New York: Doubleday.

Psychology

Claremont de Castillejo, Irene. 1997. *Knowing Woman: A Feminine Psychology.* Boston: Shambala.

Jung, Carl G. 1989. *Memories, Dreams, and Reflections.* New York: Vintage Books Edition. First published in German in 1962.

Monda, Lorena. 2000. *The Practice of Wholeness.* Placitas, NM: Golden Flower Publications.

Woodman, Marion. 1982. *Addiction to Perfection: The Still Unravished Bride.* Toronto: Inner City Books.

Woodman, Marion. 2005. *The Crown of Age.* AudioBook (CD). Boulder, CO: Sounds True, Incorporated.

Soul Work

Adyashanti. 2008. *The End of Your World: Uncensored Straight Talk on the Nature of Enlightenment.* Boulder, CO: Sounds True, Incorporated.

Hanh, Thich Nhat. 2001. *Anger: Wisdom for Cooling the Flames.* New York: Riverhead Books.

Hanh, Thich Nhat. 1987. *Being Peace.* Berkeley: Parallax Press.

McKenna, Terence. *Culture and ideology are not your friends, Opening the doors of creativity,* and many more. Podcasts available on Psychedelic Salon.

Reps, Paul and Nyogen Senzaki. 1998. *Zen Flesh, Zen Bones: A Collection of Zen and Pre-Zen Writings.* Boston, Rutland, VT, Tokyo: Tuttle Publishing. First published in 1957.

The Essential Rumi: New Expanded Edition. 1995. Translated by Coleman Barks and John Moyne. New York: HarperCollins Publishers.

Vaughan-Lee, Llewellyn. 2000. *Love is a Fire: The Sufi's Mystical Journey Home.* Point Reyes, CA: The Golden Sufi Center

Vaughan-Lee, Llewellyn. 1995. *Sufism The Transformation of the Heart.* Point Reyes, CA: The Golden Sufi Center.

Vaughan-Lee, Llewellyn. 2002. *Working With Oneness.* Point Reyes, CA: Golden Sufi Center.

Other

Deutschman, Alan. 2007. *Change or Die: The Three Keys to Change at Work and in Life.* New York: Harper Collins Publishers.

Maté, Gabor. 2003. *When The Body Says No: Exploring the Stress–Disease Connection.* Hoboken, NJ: John Wiley and Sons, 2003.

Wilson, James L. 2001. *Adrenal Fatigue: The 21st Century Stress Syndrome.* Petaluma, CA: Smart Publications.

ABOUT THE AUTHOR

Mary Saunders

Mary Saunders has been an acupuncturist in clinical practice for over 25 years. She is skilled in the integration of Oriental medicine with psychology, nutrition, and spiritual practice. Additionally, Mary uses her training as a professional coach to collaborate with her clients to improve their lives.

Mary graduated from Southwest Acupuncture College in Santa Fe, New Mexico, in 1986. She deepened her learning and practice by completing the Hakomi training in psychotherapy. The Hakomi tradition is rooted in the understanding that the body is the gateway to unconscious core beliefs that organize our experience on all levels, including our capacity for change and healing.

Co-founder of one of the first low-cost community acupuncture clinics in this country, Mary has also worked as an instructor, clinical supervisor, and the campus director for Southwest Acupuncture College, a nationally accredited acupuncture college in Boulder, Colorado.

Mary has since added mentoring and coaching to the services she offers. Mary uses a creative approach that helps her clients achieve greater self-awareness of what is important to them, align their actions with their core values, and achieve the wellness and success they desire in life.

Mary Saunders is a licensed Doctor of Oriental Medicine (DOM), a nationally certified acupuncturist with a Diplomate in Acupuncture (NCCAOM), and a Licensed Acupuncturist (LAc).

www.RhythmsofChange.net